ELECTRONIC PROJECTS FOR YOUR PC

Other Titles of Interest

ELECTRONIC PROJECTS FOR YOUR PC

by

R. A. PENFOLD

**BERNARD BABANI (publishing) LTD
THE GRAMPIANS
SHEPHERDS BUSH ROAD
LONDON W6 7NF
ENGLAND**

Please Note

Although every care has been taken with the production of this book to ensure that any projects, designs, modifications and/or programs etc. contained herewith, operate in a correct and safe manner and also that all components specified are normally available in Great Britain, the Publishers and Author do not accept responsibility in any way for the failure, including fault in design, of any project, design, modification or program to work correctly or to cause damage to any other equipment that it may be connected to or used in conjunction with, or in respect of any other damage or injury that may be so caused, nor do the Publishers accept responsibility in any way for the failure to obtain specified components.

Notice is also given that if equipment that is still under warranty is modified in any way or used or connected with home-built equipment then that warranty may be void.

© 1992 BERNARD BABANI (publishing) LTD

First Published — October 1992

British Library Cataloguing in Publication Data
Penfold, R. A.
    Electronic Projects for Your PC
    I. Title
    005.1

    ISBN 0 85934 320 0

Printed and Bound in Great Britain by Cox & Wyman Ltd, Reading

Warning

Certain circuits and projects included in this book involve mains voltages and wiring. These are not recommended for beginners or those with little knowledge or experience of working with mains and high voltages.

Preface

The IBM PCs and compatibles are now the dominant computers in virtually every aspect of micro computing. This includes the domain of do-it-yourself add-ons for computers, where PCs have been steadily taking over from the eight bit computers that were once so popular for this type of thing. In fairness to the better eight bit computers, it has to be said that they remain an excellent basis for do-it-yourself hardware add-ons. However, as more and more of the 8 bit machines fall into obsolescence, modern 16 bit alternatives have to be sought out. The PCs are the obvious choice.

I think it is true to say that most of today's 16 and 32 bit computers are not well suited to operation with user add-ons. They were simply not designed with this type of thing in mind, and in most cases have very limited potential for this type of expansion. The PCs are much more accommodating due to their expansion slots, which make it easy to add special interfaces (home constructed or otherwise). There is no built-in user port of the type found on some eight bit computers, but there is virtually unlimited potential for adding your own interfaces onto the microprocessor buses. Also, ready made PIO cards, A/D converter boards, etc., are available, which give similar facilities to the built-in user ports and analogue ports of some eight bit computers.

The circuits featured in Chapter 1 of this book provide some analogue and digital input/output ports. These are then used with the projects featured in Chapters 2 and 3. Chapter 2 is devoted to sensing and measurement, while Chapter 3 covers using the PC for control purposes. It is assumed in Chapter 1 that the reader has some knowledge of PC interfacing. Those who do not have a reasonable knowledge of this subject are advised to consult "Interfacing PCs And Compatibles" (BP272), from the same publisher and author as this publication. BP272 covers the basics of PC interfacing in some detail, including card dimensions, a detailed description of the expansion bus, bus timing, and other aspects of PC interfacing which are not covered here. It also provides a more detailed discussion of topics such as address decoding, A/D conversion, and other subjects which can only be dealt with briefly in this book. Alternatively, the projects featured in Chapters 2 and 3 could be used with any commercial interface boards which offer comparable facilities to the ports featured in Chapter 1.

The ports and projects featured here utilize the basic eight bit PC expansion bus, and are therefore suitable for use with any PC or compatible which has the standard ISA or EISA expansion bus. This means anything from the original PC through to modern modern 386 and 486 PCs.

R. A. Penfold

Contents

Chapter 1

PC INTERFACING BASICS

There is insufficient space available here for a detailed discussion on interfacing to the PC expansion bus. It is not really the purpose of this book to cover this aspect of PC interfacing anyway. This publication is more concerned with practical applications such as temperature measurement and motor speed controllers, than with address decoders and the physical characteristics of PC expansion cards. If you are not familiar with PC interfacing techniques you will need to consult a book on the subject, such as "Interfacing PCs and Compatibles" (BP272) from the same publisher and author as this publication, before proceeding with any of the circuits described here.

In this chapter we will consider circuits for simple PC digital and analogue ports. The circuits featured in the other chapters of this book interface to the PC expansion bus via these basic ports. This avoids the unnecessary repetition that would occur if each application circuit was shown complete with its address decoder and its bus interface circuit. As it is assumed that the reader is familiar with computer interfacing in general, and PC interfacing in particular, we will not consider these input and output port circuits in any great detail.

If you do not fully understand what is involved in interfacing a circuit to the PC expansion bus you should certainly not proceed further until you have gained the necessary background knowledge. Modern PCs are comparatively cheap, but they still cost a substantial sum of money in absolute terms. The chances of seriously damaging a PC due to some silly and inexperienced interfacing are probably not great, but it is still not worth the risk. **Only proceed with any PC interfacing if you are confident that you know exactly what you are doing, and that you can undertake the job competently.**

Address Decoding

The PCs are based on microprocessors from the 8086 series, all of which use separate input/output and memory maps. Although these microprocessors have provision for 16 bit addressing of input/output circuits, in the PCs only the ten least significant address lines are used. Thus there are only 1024 available addresses, and not the 65536 normally associated with the 8086 series of microprocessors. Clearly 1024 is sufficient address space for all the input/output circuits that are ever likely to be used with a PC.

This address space is divided into two 512 address blocks, and the bottom block is reserved for what is usually termed "internal" or "system" use. This means circuits that are included on the motherboard. The upper block of 512 addresses is for circuits which interface to the expansion slots, which obviously includes any user add-ons. Of course, much of this upper block of addresses is reserved for standard PC hardware, such as hard disk controller cards, serial and parallel port cards, etc.

There are some gaps in this address space which can be used for your own circuits, and the address range which is normally used is from &H300 to &H31F (768 to 799 in decimal). This address range is officially reserved for "prototype" cards. While user add-on cards might not, strictly speaking, be prototype cards, this is the address range which seems to be most apt for this type of thing. It is highly unlikely that it will cause any conflicts between your add-ons and any existing hardware in the computer, which is the main consideration.

Being practical about the situation, it is quite in order to use input/output address space which is not occupied by any other hardware in the computer. However, it will be assumed here that the &H300 to &H31F address range is to be used, and in the vast majority of cases there will be no point in using any other address space. There are thirty-two addresses in this range, with each one usable for both input and output operations. This should be sufficient for most purposes.

With only the lower ten address lines used for input/output addressing, this gives the address decoding pattern shown on page 3.

An "X" in this list indicates that this line can be decoded to either logic state. The five lines to which this applies are used

A0	X
A1	X
A2	X
A3	X
A4	X
A5	0
A6	0
A7	0
A8	1
A9	1

to select one of the thirty-two addresses in the &H300 to &H31F address range. In a minimal address decoder these lines do not have to be decoded at all, and the input/output device would then appear at all thirty-two addresses. In practice it is not a good idea to reduce the address decoding quite this far as it does not leave any room for future expansion. It is a good idea to at least decode A4 so that the address space is divided into two blocks of sixteen addresses. It is preferable to decode A3 and A4 so that the address space is divided into four blocks of eight addresses. This permits up to four user expansion cards to be used, and eight addresses per card should be sufficient.

Address decoders are not the most aptly named devices, since they invariably have to decode some control bus lines as well as address lines. In the case of PC interfacing there are three control lines which usually have to be processed by the address decoder circuit. In fact AEN absolutely always has to be processed by the address decoder, and it must be decoded to the low state (logic 0). The IOR and IOW lines respectively go low during read and write operations to the input/output addresses. IOR must therefore be decoded to the low state for an input device, but the state of IOW is unimportant. IOW must be decoded to the low state for an output circuit, but the state of IOR is then unimportant. Therefore, if an add-on device is a read only or write only device, only IOR or IOW has to be decoded, not both. Of course, many add-ons are bidirectional, and require both of these lines to be properly decoded.

Decoder Circuits

With typically only about eight to ten lines to be decoded, PC address decoder circuits do not need to be particularly complex. In fact they can be very simple indeed. One popular method of decoding is to use a circuit based on a 74LS30 eight input NAND gate. The output of a NAND gate goes low if all the inputs are high. The output goes high if there is any other combination of input states. Obviously in this application we do not require all inputs decoded to the high state, but it is merely necessary to add an inverter ahead of an input in order to make it decode to the low state.

Figure 1.1 shows the circuit diagram for a PC address decoder of the type outlined above. This decodes A4 to A9, AEN, and IOW. The output is normally high, but it goes low when any address in the range &H310 to &H31F is accessed during a write operation. If an inverter is added between address line A4 and pin 11 of IC2 the circuit will respond to any address in the range &H300 to &H30F. The 74LS14 contains six trigger/inverter circuits, making it easy to add this additional decoding if desired.

Simply connect IOR in place of IOW if the circuit must respond to read operations instead of write types. If it must respond to both read and write types, connect pin 12 of IC2 to the 0 volt supply rail and do not connect IOR and IOW to the address decoder at all. IOR and IOW are only left unprocessed by the address decoder if they will be decoded by some other circuit in the interface. This usually only occurs when an 82** series interface chip is used, or the add-on card utilizes some similar 8086 bus compatible chip.

Although this basic address decoder circuit is very simple, it works well, and is quite versatile. It can easily be modified to suit a range of address decoding requirements. Its only drawback for the home constructor is that it can be rather awkward from the constructional point of view, with an intricate pattern of printed circuit tracks often being required.

Figure 1.2 shows another simple PC address decoder circuit. This one is based on a 74LS138 3 to 8 line decoder (IC1). A 3 to 8 line decoder has eight outputs, one of which is in the active logic state while the other seven at the opposite logic state. In the case of the 74LS138 the active state for the

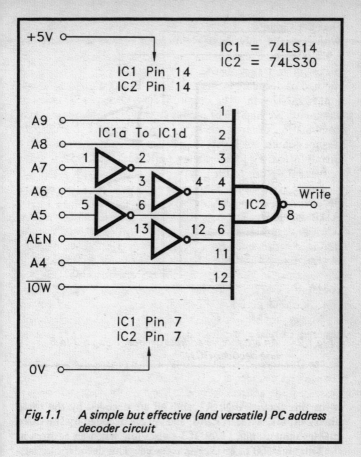

+5V o──────────────┐
                   ↓
         IC1 Pin 14   IC1 = 74LS14
         IC2 Pin 14   IC2 = 74LS30

A9 o─────────────────────── 1
A8 o─────────────────────── 2
         IC1a To IC1d
A7 o──── 1 ▷○ 2 ────────── 3
A6 o──── 3 ▷○ 4 ────────── 4
A5 o──── 5 ▷○ 6 ────────── 5   IC2   ‾Write‾
                                         o
AEN o─── 13 ▷○ 12 ───────── 6   8
A4 o─────────────────────── 11
‾IOW‾ o──────────────────── 12

         IC1 Pin 7
         IC2 Pin 7
                   ↑
0V o───────────────┘

**Fig.1.1   A simple but effective (and versatile) PC address
decoder circuit**

outputs is the low state. The outputs are numbered "0" to
"7", and the active output is dictated by the binary code on
the three inputs (e.g. 000 sends output "0" low, 001 sends
output "1" low, and so on).

Although, on the face of it, a 74LS138 can only decode
three PC bus lines, it actually has three other inputs that can
be used for decoding purposes. These are "enable" inputs,
and the outputs go to the third ("off") state unless the enable
inputs are at the correct states. There are two negative enable
inputs (pins 4 and 5), and one positive enable input (pin 6).

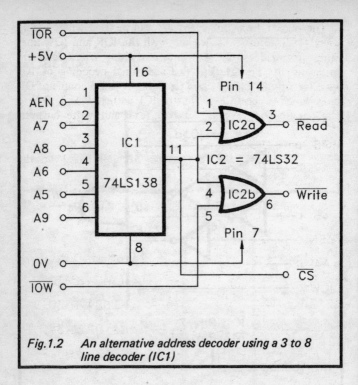

*Fig.1.2 An alternative address decoder using a 3 to 8
line decoder (IC1)*

In this circuit AEN, A7, and A8 are decoded by the three
binary inputs, while A5, A6, and A9 are decoded by the three
enable inputs. Pin 11 of IC1 pulses low when an address in
the range &H300 to &H31F is accessed. This decoder obviously responds to all the available address space, which is unaccept-
able if you will want to use this address space for more than
one add-on card. However, if necessary some extra decoding
can be added ahead of IC1. For example, rather than connecting A5 direct to pin 5 of IC1, it could be processed together
with A3 and A4 by an additional gate circuit, so that the
decoder as a whole would respond to an eight address block
within the &H300 to &H31F address range. The design of the
additional gate circuit would determine which of the four
address blocks the circuit responded to.

The output from pin 11 of IC1 can be used where a chip select ("CS") output is needed, with the IOR and IOW lines being processed by the main interface chip. Where read and write outputs are needed, the additional decoding of IC2 must be included. This extra decoding is just a couple of OR gates which process the output of IC1 with IOR and IOW to provide separate (negative active) read and write outputs.

Multi-Output Decoder

Figure 1.3 shows another address decoder based on the

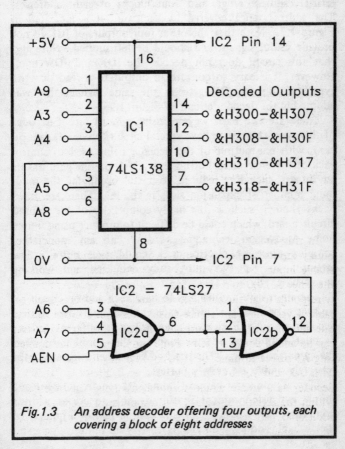

Fig.1.3   An address decoder offering four outputs, each covering a block of eight addresses

74LS138 3 to 8 line decoder, but this one utilizes four of its outputs. It decodes eight lines of the PC's expansion bus, which obviously requires some additional gating ahead of the 74LS138. This decoding is provided by two of the 3 input NOR gates of IC2. These are wired so that an OR action is obtained. When A6, A7, and AEN are all low a negative enable signal is supplied to IC1.

This extra gating frees two of IC1's binary inputs which no longer have to decode A7 and A8. They can instead be used to decode A3 and A4, which breaks the &H300 to &H31F address range into four blocks of eight addresses. The address range covered by each output is indicated in Figure 1.3. Note that the other four outputs of IC1 do not provide useful signals, and should be left unused. Note also that this circuit does not decode the IOR and IOW lines. However, it is easy to convert an output to a read or write type by using an OR gate in the same manner that was adopted in the decoder circuit of Figure 1.2.

There are two basic ways of using a multi-output decoder of this type. One is to have several circuits on one expansion card, with one output of the decoder being used to control each of these circuits. Putting everything on one card has its advantages, including reduced cost, and occupying the minimum number of expansion slots in the PC. There are drawbacks though, such as the likely complexity of the printed circuit board, which could be difficult to produce using simple home production techniques. Also, with any moderately complex piece of electronics it could take quite a few attempts to get everything fully debugged and working correctly.

The alternative approach is to have each add-on circuit on its own expansion card, with each card having its own address decoder circuit. Each card then utilizes a different address decoder output and address range so that conflicts between the cards are avoided. This method keeps each expansion card relatively simple and easy to perfect.

Even if you only have an immediate requirement for one simple expansion card, it is still advisable to use an address decoder circuit which places that card in half or a quarter of the available address space. This leaves your options open, and makes it easy to add further user add-ons if you should wish to do so at some later date (which you probably will). By using all thirty-two addresses you would be painting yourself into the proverbial corner.

PIO

An address decoder is of little practical value on its own, and some additional circuitry is needed in order to provide parallel input lines and latching output lines. These can be provided using standard TTL chips and techniques, or special PIO interface chips. I generally prefer to use a specialist PIO chip as one of these provides plenty of lines which can be used as inputs or outputs. Also, provided the chip is one that is intended for operation with the microprocessor in the computer, simple interfacing and reliable operation are assured.

The PIO chip usually selected for use on PC expansion cards is the 8255A. This is a type which was popular for use with 8 bit home computers based on the Z80A microprocessor, and it should be familiar to anyone who has produced add-ons for the Sinclair Spectrum, ZX81, etc. It has three 8 bit parallel input/output ports which are named ports "A", "B", and "C". This gives some twenty-four input/output lines, which is better than most other PIO chips. On the other hand, it is only fair to point out that in certain respects this chip is not quite as accommodating as some other parallel interface chips.

Whereas some PIO chips permit each line to be individually programmed as an input or an output, with the 8255A all the lines of each port must be set to the same function. The only exception is that port C can be set to a split mode where the upper nibble operates as four inputs and the lower nibble acts as four outputs (or vice versa). The general idea is that port C should be used in this split mode to provide handshake lines for ports A and B. This gives a situation not much different to other PIO chips such as the 6821 where there are only two 8 bit ports, but there are two additional lines on each port which are specifically designed to permit easy handshaking. The 8255A provides more lines for handshaking or general use, but they can be slightly more difficult to use in handshaking applications.

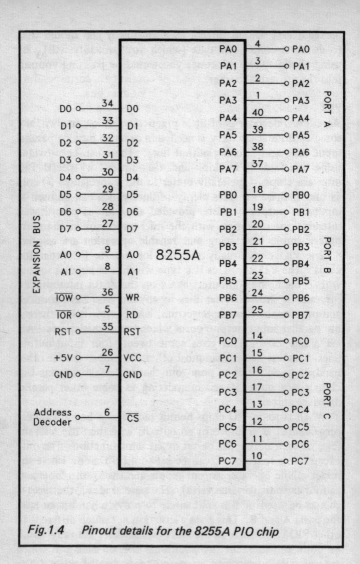

Fig.1.4   Pinout details for the 8255A PIO chip

Figure 1.4 gives pinout details for the 8255A, and it also shows the correct method of connecting it to the PC expansion bus. The negative chip select input (pin 6) is fed from the address decoder, which must obviously be a type that provides negative output pulses (as are the address decoder circuits featured earlier in this chapter). The RST, −IOW, and −IOR lines of the control bus all connect to corresponding terminals of the 8255A, as does the 8 bit data bus.

There are two register select inputs on the 8255A, which would normally connect to A0 and A1. Accordingly, they are called A0 and A1 rather than RS0 and RS1 (or something similar). If the address decoder responds (say) to eight addresses from &H308 to &H30F, then the 8255A will occupy four addresses from &H308 to &H30B. It will also occupy addresses from &H30C to &H30F in the form of one set of echoes. Therefore, these addresses would be unusable for other purposes. Of course, the 8255A could be placed in just four addresses with no echoes, but in most cases there will not be a great enough shortage of address space to make this worthwhile.

The outputs of the 8255A are latching types which are compatible with 74LS** and 74HCT** TTL devices. The inputs are also compatible with these devices. In fact the device seems to work reliably with most logic devices, including most CMOS types.

8255 Programming
There is insufficient space available here to go into great detail about all the 8255 operating modes, and methods of using this device. Anyone using practically any computer peripheral chip would be well advised to obtain the relevant data sheet, and I would certainly recommend this for anyone who is going to use a chip as complex as the 8255A. However, here we will consider the basic ways of using this interface chip, which should at least get you started, and may be all that you need in order to use the chip effectively in your particular applications.

The 8255A has four read/write registers. Three of these are ports A, B, and C. Obviously each one of these would normally be used only as a read register or a write type, depending on whether its port has been set as an input or an output type. The exception to this is when port C is used in the split mode of operation, and it is then a form of read/write register. The fourth register is a control type, and data would normally only be written to this. You can read data from this register, but it will not furnish anything meaningful. If you need a record of what has been written to the control register, a byte of RAM must be used to store a copy of each control number that is written to this register.

If we assume that the 8255A is at the example address range mentioned earlier (&H308 to &H30B), then the base addresses of the four registers would be as follows:-

Hex Address	Dec. Address	Register
&H308	776	Port A
&H309	777	Port B
&H30A	778	Port C
&H30B	779	Control

Using the ports is straightforward enough, but the control register is a bit tricky to fully master. There are three modes of operation for the 8255A, which have been designated modes 0, 1, and 2. Mode 0 is the most simple, and is the one you should use when initially experimenting with the 8255A. In this mode the ports operate as simple input/output types, with the only complication that port C can operate in the split mode (one nibble as inputs and the other nibble as outputs).

The required operating mode is set by bits five to seven of the control register. Bit seven is set high in order to enable the operating mode to be changed. Be careful to set this bit high, as the control register operates in a totally different manner if this bit is set to zero. Bits five and six control the operating mode. This table shows how this scheme of things operates.

Mode	Bit 7	Bit 6	Bit 5
0	1	0	0
1	1	0	1
2	1	1	0
2	1	1	1

As will be apparent from this table, there are two control codes which select mode 2. It does not matter which one you

12

use, the effect on the 8255A is exactly the same. These bits only control the mode of port A and the upper nibble of port C. Port B and the lower nibble of port C are controlled by bit 2 of the control register. This is either high for mode 1 operation, or low if you require mode 0 operation. Mode 2 is not applicable to these ports, and so one bit is all that is needed for their mode control.

Bits zero, one, three, and four are used to control the functions of the ports (i.e. whether they operate as inputs or outputs). This operates in the following manner:-

Control Bit	Port	Dec. Value When High
0	C Lower	1
1	B	2
3	C Upper	8
4	A	16

In order to set a port as an output type the control bit is set to zero. Setting a control bit to 1 obviously sets its respective port as an input type. Those who are used to the 6522, 6821, etc., should note that this works the opposite way round to the data direction registers of these chips.

When writing to the control register you must set the mode of operation and the port directions in a single write operation. You can not write to bits five to seven first, and then bits zero, one, three, and four. However, working out the right control register values is not difficult. For mode 0 operation bits five and six are low, and bit seven is high. To set bit seven high a decimal value of 128 is required. The table provided previously shows the decimal value needed for each control bit when it is set high (i.e. when its port is to be set as an input). A value of zero is, of course, needed for any bits that will be set low.

Simply take the values given in the table for the ports that are to be set as inputs, and then add 128 to the total of these values. You then have the value to write to the control register. For example, assume that port A and both nibbles of port C are to be set as inputs. The values for these ports as inputs are sixteen, eight, and one. This gives a total of twenty-five. Adding 128 to this gives a grand total of 153, which is the value that must be written to the control register. In GW BASIC, and using the example port addresses mentioned previously, this value would be written to the control register using the instruction:-

OUT 779,153

You can use hexadecimal addresses with GW BASIC if you prefer, but remember that hexadecimal numbers are indicated using both the "&H" prefix, not just the "&" prefix used in some languages. Numbers having just the "&" prefix may well be accepted, as I think that these are interpreted by GW BASIC as octal (base eight) numbers. This has led me into some time-consuming errors in the past as I tend to use just the "&" prefix from force of habit (having mainly used a BBC computer for interfacing in the past). Consequently, I now always use decimal input/output addresses when using GW BASIC.

For many purposes mode 0 operation will suffice. For example, there are many applications which do not require any form of handshaking. These include such things as driving digital to analogue converters, relay drivers, etc., and reading simple sensors. For applications of this type you only need simple input and output lines, and there is no point in using anything beyond mode 0.

Where handshaking is needed, setting port C for split operation to provide the handshake input/output lines will often suffice. This does not provide edge triggered inputs or anything of this type, but simple input and output lines will usually be sufficient. Remember that where necessary you can always use some external signal processing, such as a pulse stretcher or shortener, in order to make things more reliable. For instance, if an output is providing very brief pulses, a pulse stretcher might provide a signal which can be read more reliably, with no pulses passing undetected by the handshake input.

Where complex handshaking is needed it might be better to resort to mode 1 operation. This uses port A and port B as eight bit input/output ports, and six lines of port C to act as strobed handshake lines and interrupt control signals (three lines per port). Mode 2 provides strobed bidirectional operation through port A, with five lines of port C acting as what I suppose is a sort of control bus. This is not a mode that I have ever used, and it is presumably only needed for a few specialised applications. Anyway, to fully get to grips with the 8255A you really need to study the data sheet and then experiment a little.

Figure 1.5 shows the functions of the 8255A control register bits in diagrammatic form, and this should be useful for reference purposes when programming this device.

D/A Converters

Computers deal only with digital information, but the real world is very much an analogue one. In order to control the speed of electric motors, the intensity of lights, etc., it is necessary to convert digital values from the converter into corresponding voltages. Via suitable voltage controlled circuits the computer can then control practically anything you like. Strictly speaking the control provided by such a system is not analogue in that it provides stepped control, rather than the continuously variable control of a true analogue system.

The key to success with a digital control system is to have high enough resolution (i.e. a large enough number of steps) to give sufficiently precise control. If the resolution is high enough, the stepped method of control might not be apparent to anyone using the system. In some applications high resolution control it not really needed. Although the steps from one speed to the next (or whatever) might be pretty obvious, this may not detract from the performance of the system. It is a matter of carefully considering each case on its own merits, but if in doubt, always go for a high level of resolution. A certain amount of overkill will not do any harm, whereas even a slight lack of resolution can render a system of little practical value.

For most purposes an 8 bit digital-to-analogue converter is more than adequate. An 8 bit converter gives 256 different output levels (including 0 volts). I have tried a number of 8 bit digital-to-analogue converter chips over the last ten years or so, and I find that the ZN426E is about the most simple to

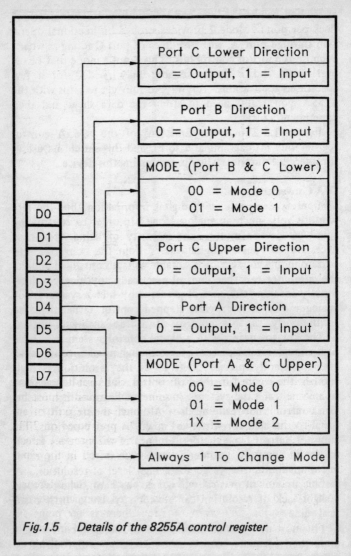

Fig.1.5   Details of the 8255A control register

use, but it is also one of the most effective of these chips. Figure 1.6 shows the circuit diagram for a simple digital-to-analogue converter based on this device.

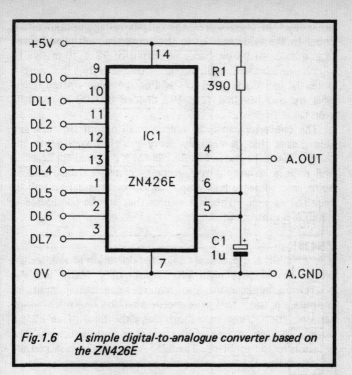

Fig.1.6 *A simple digital-to-analogue converter based on the ZN426E*

The first point to note here is that this circuit does not connect direct to the PC expansion bus. Instead it must be driven from a latching output port, such as one port of an 8255A, or a simple 8 bit latching output port based on TTL chips. Alternatively, the ZN428E (which will interface direct to the PC data bus) can be used, as described in the next section of this book.

The maximum output voltage is equal to the reference potential fed to pin 5. This could be fed from an external reference source, but in most cases there is no point in doing so. The ZN426E contains a highly accurate and stable 2.55 volt reference generator which has its output available at pin 6. This requires discrete load resistor R1 and decoupling capacitor C1. A maximum output voltage of 2.55 volts is a convenient one, as it represents a resolution of exactly 10 millivolts. In other words, the output voltage in millivolts is equal to the value written to the converter multiplied by ten (e.g. a value of 98 produces an output of 98 × 10 millivolts, which equals 980 millivolts). Alternatively, the output potential in volts is given by dividing the value written to the port by one hundred (e.g. 198 divided by 100 equals 1.98 volts).

The converter can only supply small output currents, and this means that in virtually every practical application the output has to be buffered. In fact most practical applications will require an output voltage range of other than 0 to 2.55 volts, and some voltage amplification or attenuation will be required as well. This is a subject that will be considered in detail in a subsequent chapter.

ZN428E

The ZN426E is a practical choice for operation in an interface which has a spare eight bit output port. Many analogue conversion applications also require some digital inputs or outputs, for such things as motor direction control, position sensors, etc. Using something along the lines of an 8255A with a ZN426E on one of its ports then represents a practical solution to the problem. The 8255A provides an easy method of interfacing the converter, and it has plenty of spare input/output lines for control and sensing purposes.

Where an analogue output is all that is required, the ZN428E probably represents a more practical choice. This is virtually identical to the ZN426E, but it has a built-in eight bit data latch which enables it to be directly interfaced to most computer data buses, including the PC data bus. Figure 1.7 shows the circuit diagram for a digital-to-analogue converter based on the ZN428E.

This is much the same as the circuit of Figure 1.6, but in this case the data inputs of the converter chip are fed from the data lines of the PC's expansion bus. Also, there is a negative "Write" input which must be fed with negative latching pulses from the address decoder circuit. The ZN428E has separate analogue and digital ground terminals (pins 8 and 9), and these do not have to be at precisely the same voltage. However, in most applications there is no advantage in having them

18

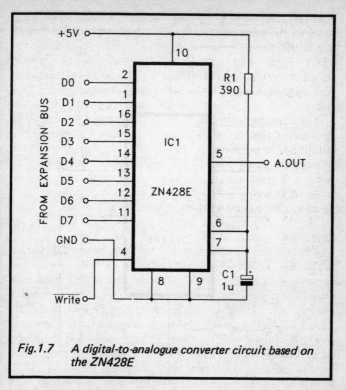

Fig.1.7 A digital-to-analogue converter circuit based on the ZN428E

at differential potentials, and they are then both connected to the digital ground.

Analogue-to-Digital

Conversion from an analogue quantity to a digital value tends to be rather more complex than conversion in the opposite direction. Fortunately, most of the added complexity is hidden away inside the converter chip, and is not something that the user has to worry about. You can not completely ignore the extra complexity though, and in virtually all analogue-to-digital converter applications some form of handshaking is required. Without at least some very basic handshaking the data read from an analogue-to-digital converter is likely to be little better than a series of random numbers.

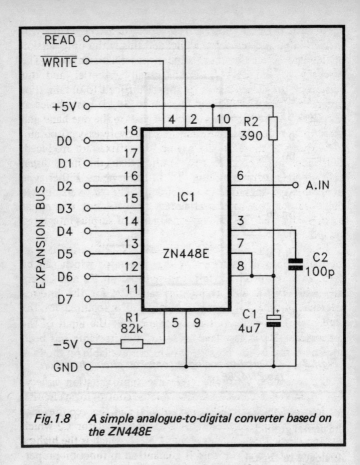

Fig.1.8   A simple analogue-to-digital converter based on the ZN448E

Figure 1.8 shows the circuit diagram for an analogue-to-digital converter based on the Ferranti ZN448E. There are actually two chips which are identical to the ZN448E, the ZN447E and the ZN449E, which can also be used in this circuit. The only difference between these three chips is their guaranteed level of accuracy. These are 0.25, 0.5, and 1 lsb respectively for the ZN447E, ZN448E, and the ZN449E.

As one would expect, the higher the guaranteed accuracy of the chip, the greater its cost. The actual cost differences are quite high, so unless high accuracy is really needed, the

ZN449E is the best choice. In practice the extra accuracy of the ZN448E is often worthwhile, and this is the only version of the chip offered by most component retailers anyway. The accuracy of the ZN447E is not usually essential, and this version of the device seems to be very difficult to obtain. For general use the ZN448E would seem to be the best choice as it offers a good compromise between cost on the one hand and performance on the other, and it is relatively easy to obtain.

Versions of these devices having "J" suffixes are produced, and these have ceramic cases rather than the more usual plastic encapsulations of the "E" suffix devices. Either type is suitable for operation in this circuit. The "E" versions are the ones sold by most component retailers, but you might occasionally find the "J" versions in lists of surplus integrated circuits.

Like the ZN426E and ZN428E, the ZN448E series have an internal 2.55 volt reference voltage generator which can be used, as here, to set the full scale sensitivity. R2 and C1 are the load resistor and decoupling capacitor for the internal reference source. A negative supply rail is required for the "tail" resistor of the voltage comparator at the input of the converter. R1 is the "tail" resistor, and its value has been chosen to suit a −5 volt supply (which is available on the PC's expansion bus).

The converter is of the successive approximation variety, and it requires a clock generator for the control logic circuits. An internal clock oscillator is available, and this requires just one discrete component. This is timing capacitor C2 which sets the clock frequency at about 1 MHz, which is the highest frequency at which the chip is guaranteed to function properly. However, in practice it is usually possible to obtain faster operation by making C2 lower in value. It is a matter of using trial and error to find the lowest value which gives correct operation of the converter. In some cases the self-capacitance of the device seems to be adequate, and provides a clock frequency of about 2 MHz.

It takes a maximum of nine clock pulses to provide a conversion, which is obviously about 9 μs at a clock frequency of 1 MHz. This works out at a maximum of around 110,000 conversions per second. Whichever way you look at it, this is more than adequate for most applications, including audio digitising. Many applications only require one reading every few seconds. Pushing the speed of the device to the limits is therefore unnecessary in most cases.

As pointed out previously, some form of handshaking is needed in order to get an analogue-to-digital converter to do anything worthwhile in practice. In its most basic form this just consists of an output which pulses the negative "Write" input low in order to start a conversion. This pulse can be provided by the negative write output of an address decoder, and a conversion is then started simply by writing a "dummy" value to the appropriate address (e.g. OUT &H300,0). The "dummy" value can be any legal value, which means any integer value from 0 to 255 (I always use 0 for "dummy" write operations).

It is essential that the converter is not read before the conversion has been completed. There is a status output at pin 1, and this goes low while a conversion is in progress. Obviously this could be read by a digital input line, and a software routine could be used to provide a hold-off until this output went high.

In practice it is usually easier to ignore this status output and instead opt for a timing loop to provide a hold-off. Remember that conversions take no more than about 9 μs, and that a timing loop to provide a hold-off of at least this duration will ensure that valid data is read from the converter. It is also worth bearing in mind that the speed of many PC languages is such that sending a start conversion pulse and then immediately taking a reading will give perfectly satisfactory results. In particular, interpreted BASICs seem to be nothing like fast enough to produce premature readings.

The ZN448E has tristate outputs which can interface directly onto the PC's data bus. The address decoder must provide a negative "read" pulse to pin 2 of IC1 in order to take the outputs to the active state and force data onto the bus. Alternatively, the device can be interfaced via an 8255A or similar input/output ports. The data outputs are then fed to an 8 bit input port and pin 2 is tied to ground. The "write" pulse could still be provided by an address decoder circuit, or pin 4 of IC1 could be fed from a digital output of the PIA.

In order to provide optimum accuracy the ZN448E requires a discrete zero offset circuit. This trims out the slight errors that otherwise occur at low readings. This is a topic which will be dealt with in a subsequent chapter which deals with using the converter in practical applications. Using signal processing to obtain different full scale values will also be covered.

Chapter 2

SENSING AND MEASUREMENT

Once a computer has been equipped with some digital inputs and an analogue input port it can be used in a wide range of sensing and measurement applications. However, the real world will rarely provide electrical signals that are suitable for direct connection to the computer's ports, and some extra interfacing is required for virtually any practical application. In most cases this extra interfacing can be quite simple.

Voltage Measurement
Voltage measurement using a computer might seem to be an "over the top" method of handling things, and for many voltage measurement applications I suppose it would be. On the other hand, a computerised voltage measuring system can be programmed to take readings automatically at preset intervals. Alternatively, the system can constantly monitor voltages, record the results, and sound an alarm if readings stray outside certain limits, or provide a variety of similar monitoring applications.

This type of monitoring is more than a little helpful where newly designed circuits must be tested for short to medium term stability, or when trying to trace the problem in a piece of electronic equipment that has an intermittent fault. Manual checking and monitoring in these circumstances can take a vast amount of man-hours, and can be a bit tedious for whoever gets the job of writing down all the results.

The analogue-to-digital converter circuit featured in Chapter 1 (Figure 1.8) can be used for voltage measurement, but its input voltage range of 0 to 2.55 volts is obviously unsuitable for many voltage monitoring purposes. Also, as pointed out in Chapter 1, the converter chip does not have built-in zero offsetting, and requires an external circuit in order to achieve optimum accuracy at low readings.

Figure 2.1 shows the circuit diagram for an attenuator and zero offset adjustment circuit for use with the ZN448 series

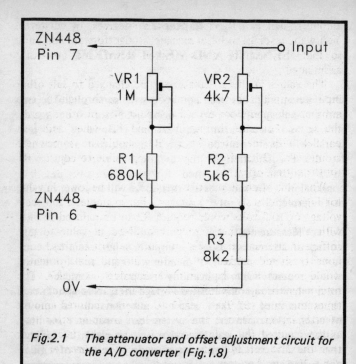

*Fig.2.1   The attenuator and offset adjustment circuit for
the A/D converter (Fig.1.8)*

of converters. The offset problem is simply that readings tend
to be fractionally too low. In order to counteract this a small
positive voltage must be fed to the input of the converter.
This is the purpose of VR1 and R1. For this system to work
properly the offset circuit must be feeding into a suitable
input resistance. VR2, R2, and R3 act as an attenuator which
sets the required input sensitivity, and it also provides a
suitable resistance into which the offset circuit can operate.

With the specified circuit values the input sensitivity is
about 5 volts full scale. VR2 permits the full scale voltage to
be adjusted somewhat either side of this figure, and the
logical choice for the full scale sensitivity is 5.1 volts. This
gives readings which increment in sensible steps of 20 millivolts (0.02 volts). When using analogue-to-digital converters
always try to avoid having readings that increment in odd

amounts such as 0.0235 volts, 0.567 degrees, or whatever. You want readings to be in sensible, straightforward amounts, so that they can be quickly noted down, and are easily assimilated.

The values in the attenuator can be changed to suit other input sensitivities, but the parallel resistance through the two arms of the attenuator should be about 4k. In other words, the series resistance through VR2 and R2, when added in parallel with the resistance of R3, should be somewhere around 4k. Otherwise it may not be possible to adjust VR1 for the correct offset.

What this means in practice is that R3 will be lower in value for higher full scale input voltages. For example, a full scale voltage of 10.2 volts would require R3 to be reduced to 5k6, with VR2 and R2 being roughly doubled in value to give sufficient attenuation (values of 10k for both of these components should suffice). A 20.4 volt full scale potential would require R3 to be even lower in value − say 4k7. The total value through VR2 and R2 would need to be about seven times this value (32.9k) in order to give the required amount of attenuation. On the face of it I have made an error here, as the required full scale potential is some eight times higher than the 2.55 volt full scale sensitivity of the converter (2.55 × 8 = 20.4), and not seven times this value.

The salient point here is that for every volt developed across R3, seven volts must be produced across VR2 and R2. For every eight volts across the entire resistor network, one volt will then be developed across R3, giving the required eight to one attenuation ratio. The correct value for the input resistance is therefore equal to the value of R3 multiplied by one less than the required attenuation factor. Suitable practical values for our example full scale potential of 20.4 volts would therefore be 27k for R2, and 10k for VR2.

For full scale voltages of about 50 volts or more it would be necessary to reduce R2 to a value of 4k3. In theory there is no upper limit to the maximum input voltage that can be accommodated, but in reality you have to bear in mind the practical limitations of the components. Unless you use special high voltage types, these are likely to impose a limit of about 250 volts (the retailer's catalogue should give maximum voltage ratings for the fixed and preset resistors they sell). **You should not try to measure potentials of more than about 100 volts unless you are sure you know what you are doing, and all the necessary safety precautions are taken.**

Adjustment

Before adjusting VR1 for the proper offset it is necessary to set the correct full scale sensitivity using VR2. Ideally this should be done by feeding the circuit with an input voltage equal to the full scale value, or 5.1 volts in this example. VR2 is then carefully adjusted for a stable reading of 5.1 volts. However, quite accurate results should be obtained using any calibration voltage that is fairly close to the full scale value. For example, if the PC's +5 volt supply is measured at 4.96 volts, then this could be used as the calibration voltage, with VR2 being adjusted for a stable reading of 4.96 volts.

In order to adjust VR1 properly it is necessary to feed an input voltage to the circuit that is equal to half the resolution of the circuit. In this case the resolution is 20 millivolts, and a voltage of 10 millivolts must therefore be fed to the input of the circuit. A suitable voltage can be provided using the simple potential divider network of Figure 2.2 plus the PC's +5 volt supply. With this circuit feeding into the input of the converter circuit, VR1 is adjusted for an unstable reading that fluctuates between 0 and 1. It is then a good idea to check the full scale accuracy of the circuit, and if necessary, recalibrate the unit again using VR2.

It is worth mentioning that the offset errors are quite small. In fact the error is typically only 5 millivolts at the input of the converter, which compares with a resolution of 10 millivolts here. Obviously this error is quite small, but it is still significant on very low readings. Nevertheless, in some applications there may well be no point in bothering with the offset circuit. In particular, in some applications the minimum reading could well be somewhere around half the full scale value, and the effect of the offset circuit would be insignificant in such cases.

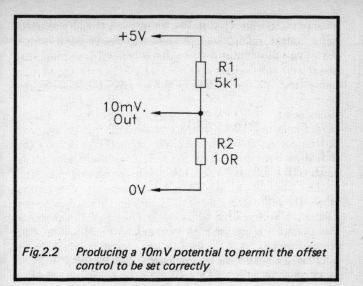

Fig.2.2   Producing a 10mV potential to permit the offset control to be set correctly

Software

Although the BASIC programming language has received a fair amount of criticism over the years, this is almost certainly the best language to use when testing computer projects. An interpreted BASIC, or a BASIC compiler with some sort of "direct" mode, are especially good for general testing purposes. In fact BASIC languages are well suited to production of the final software for most computer projects. The only proviso is that the BASIC must be one that provides access to the input/output map, or it will obviously not be possible to gain access to your add-on devices.

The simple example programs given in this book are all in GW BASIC, and should work equally well as QBASIC programs if you have MS/DOS 5.0 or higher. They should also compile properly using Microsoft Quick BASIC, but there might be slight problems in some cases due to the higher operating speed of compiled programs. However, a few minor adjustments should soon sort out any speed problems that might occur.

This listing is for a program that will display the input voltage on the screen. It is assumed here (and in the other listings in this book) that the converter is at address &H300 (768 decimal). Obviously this address must be altered if you are using a different address for the converter.

```
10  REM voltage reading program
20  CLS
30  OUT 768,0
40  X = INP(768)
50  X = X/50
60  CLS
70  PRINT X"volts"
80  FOR D = 1 TO 5000
90  NEXT D
100 A$ = INKEY$
110 IF LEN(A$) = 0 THEN GOTO 30
```

Line 20 simply clears the screen, and the next line then initiates a conversion. Line 40 reads the converter and places the returned value in variable "X". The speed of the program is such that no hold-off should be needed in order to avoid a premature reading. It is assumed in line 50 that the full scale voltage is 5.1 volts, and readings are therefore divided by 50 to give a display in volts.

The screen is cleared at line 60, which means that readings are always displayed in the top left-hand corner of the screen. Line 70 actually displays the reading, and adds the word "volts" after the voltage figure. No space character is needed at the beginning of this string, because GW BASIC automatically puts in a space at the end of variable "X". Lines 80 and 90 simply provide a delay which slows the program down to something like one or two readings per second. This gives a steadier display with the simple methods used in this program. With more sophisticated programming techniques this would probably be unnecessary, and the program could be allowed to loop at maximum speed.

The keyboard is read at line 100, and any character read from the keyboard is placed into string variable "A$". The program normally loops back from line 110 to line 30 so that readings are taken indefinitely. However, if any character key is pressed, the program will simply terminate at line

110. With any program that loops continuously you should remember to provide a "get-out clause" so that things can be brought to a tidy conclusion.

In some applications you may simply wish to have a program which, like this one, simply displays readings. Remember though, that with a computerised measuring system there are almost endless possibilities. For example, readings can be taken at regular intervals, stored in memory, and displayed later in graph form. Another possibility is for readings to be taken at regular intervals and printed out on the system printer. It is a matter of tailoring things to suit your particular application.

Buffered Input

The circuit of Figure 2.1 is satisfactory for some purposes, but it only works well if it is fed from a fairly low source impedance. Like an ordinary analogue multimeter, it requires a significant input current. In analogue multimeter terms, it has a rather poor sensitivity of only about 2k to 3k per volt. This can result in loading on the test point and a substantial reduction at that point in the circuit while the measurements are being made. More consistent and reliable results can be obtained by adding a buffer stage ahead of the converter. This gives a very high input resistance, and a minimal input current. Like a high resistance analogue voltmeter or a digital multimeter, this ensures that there is no significant loading on the circuit under test, and that accurate results are obtained.

Figure 2.3 shows the circuit diagram for a buffer stage that can be added ahead of this converter to provide a much higher input resistance. The input resistance of the MOSFET operational amplifier used in the circuit is over a million megohms, but in practice the circuit as a whole has a substantially lower input resistance. This is due to the need for bias and attenuation resistors at the input, which shunt the input resistance down to what is typically about 10 megohms or so. This is clearly a massive reduction on the basic input resistance of the operational amplifier, but it is still high enough to give good results when the unit is used to make measurements on normal circuits.

31

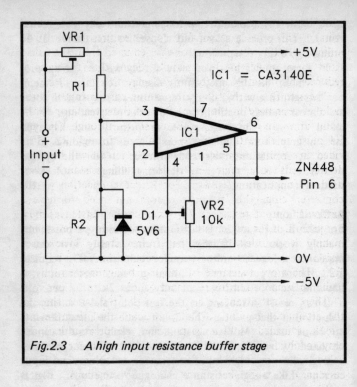

Fig.2.3   A high input resistance buffer stage

The circuit is basically just a non-inverting amplifier with 100% negative feedback so that it has unity voltage gain. VR2 is an offset null control, and it is used to compensate for offset voltages in IC1 and in the converter circuit. R2 biases the non-inverting input of IC1 to the 0 volt supply rail and it also forms the shunt arm of the input attenuator. R1 and VR1 form the other arm of the attenuator. D1 is not an essential part of the circuit, and its purpose is to provide protection for IC1 if there is an excessive input voltage.

Some simple mathematics is all that is involved in deriving suitable values for VR1, R1, and R2. First you must calculate the ratio of the input voltage to the full scale voltage of the converter. Suppose that a full scale potential of 10 volts is required. It would be sensible to settle for a full scale value of 10.2 volts, since this is exactly four times the full scale input voltage of the converter (2.55 volts × 4 = 10.2 volts). This gives a reasonably convenient resolution of 40 millivolts (0.04 volts). Next one is deducted from the calculated ratio, which in this example means that the ratio is reduced from four to one to three to one.

The significance of this three to one ratio is that it is the ratio of resistance in the input arm of the attenuator to the shunt arm. In other words, the resistance through VR1 and R1 must be three times higher than that through R2. Provided this resistance ratio is correct, the circuit will have the desired sensitivity, regardless of the actual resistance values used. Unlike an attenuator for direct connection to the converter chip, this attenuator does not need to have a particular output resistance. In practice the resistances must be quite high, or the circuit will have a low input resistance, making it pointless to use the buffer stage. The input resistance is equal to the series resistance of VR1, R1, and R2. The input resistance of IC1 can be ignored as it is so high in comparison to the resistance of R2.

There is an advantage in making the resistance through the attenuator network as high as possible so that the test circuit is loaded as little as possible. In practice it is not easy to obtain resistors of more than about 10 megohms in value, which means that it is difficult to achieve an input resistance of more than about 10 to 20 megohms. This is sufficient to give good results in virtually all practical situations though, and represents what will often be an input current of under one microamp.

In this case a value of 3M3 for R2 would seem to be about right. This would give a combined resistance for R1 and VR1 of 9.9 megohms (3.3 megohms × 3 = 9.9 megohms). Provided close tolerance resistors are used for R1 and R2, values of 9M1 and 2M2 should suffice for R1 and VR1 respectively. Using ordinary 10% resistors this set of values might not give a wide enough adjustment range to permit the correct full scale value to be set. Values of 8M2 and 4M7 would then be a better choice. However, in the interest of good long term stability it is better to use good quality resistors, and to have the value of VR1 fairly low in relation to that of R1.

Adjustment

Adjustment starts with VR2, which must initially be given a setting that provides a small positive output voltage. It is then adjusted just far enough to give stable readings of zero from the converter. Be careful not to adjust it any further than is really necessary, as this would result in low readings being substantially too low. The circuit must next be connected to an input voltage which represents something close to the full scale value of the circuit. VR1 is then adjusted for the correct reading from the converter.

Strictly speaking, no further adjustment should then be required. However, it is always a good idea to repeat the adjustment procedure once or twice to make sure that everything is setup as accurately as possible.

Low Voltage Measurement

It is possible to measure quite low voltages if the converter circuit is preceded by a d.c. amplifier. I would not recommend trying to use high levels of gain to measure really small voltages if this can be avoided. There are two main problems when using sensitive d.c. measuring equipment, which are drift and noise problems. The problem of drift need not be a major one provided the operating temperature is reasonably stable. Also, there are special instrumentation grade operational amplifiers which can be used in applications where high d.c. stability is essential. These devices are relatively expensive though.

The noise problem can be a more difficult one to tackle. First there is the noise of the operational amplifier itself. In many cases this will not be severe enough to cause any major difficulties. However, one of the special low noise devices can be used where the innate noise of the amplifier becomes a major problem. These ultra low noise operational amplifiers are much more expensive than the "bog standard" types, but they can produce a reduction in the noise level by a factor of ten or more.

In my experience the main difficulty is noise that is picked up at the input of the circuit by some form of stray coupling. This can be caused by earthing problems, or simple stray coupling to non-screened input wiring. Obviously this type of

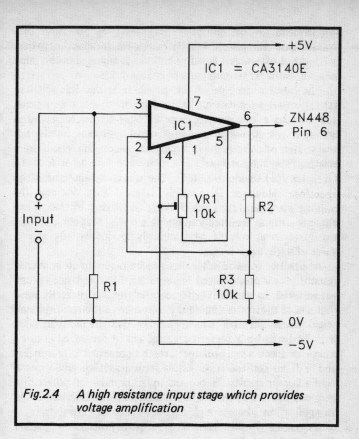

Fig.2.4   A high resistance input stage which provides voltage amplification

thing can be minimised by using a carefully designed layout, using good quality screened cables, etc., but it can be more difficult than you might think to eliminate the problem. Digital circuits, especially computers, produce large amounts of electrical noise which somehow seems to find its way into any nearby circuit that is operating at low signal levels.

Where low voltages really must be measured, a simple d.c. amplifier of the type shown in Figure 2.4 is needed. Although a CA3140E is specified for IC1, the circuit should work properly using a μA741C or any genuinely μA741C compatible operational amplifier. The circuit is just a standard non-inverting mode amplifier having R1 as the input bias resistor and R2 plus R3 as the negative feedback network. VR1 is the offset null control, and this is adjusted in the same manner as the offset null control in Figure 2.3.

The input resistance of the circuit is set by R1, and it is simply equal to whatever value is given to this component. This can be a megohm or more in value if desired, but it is advisable not to use a very high input resistance unless it is really necessary. A high input resistance can result in a relatively high noise level. The gain of the circuit is equal to (R2 plus R3) divided by R3. The required value for R2 is therefore calculated by first deducting 1 from the required voltage gain, and then multiplying this figure by 10k. For example, if the required voltage gain is 45, deducting 1 from this gives an answer of 44. Multiplying this by 10k gives a value of 440k for R2.

In practice R2 will often have to be made up from a fixed resistor plus a preset wired in series, so that the resistance can be adjusted to precisely the required figure. Bear in mind that the gain error is double the tolerance of the resistors used (e.g. 2% even if 1% resistors are used). Also, the required value is unlikely to be a preferred value, and it would have to be made up from a network of several resistors. Using a preset and a fixed resistor is an easier solution which will provide very accurate results. In our example, the value of 440k could be made using a 390k resistor in series with a 100k preset. In an application where a high degree of accuracy is important it is always worthwhile using a good quality preset — possibly even a multi-turn type.

The bandwidth of the amplifier is quite wide, and is equal to the gain bandwidth product of the operational amplifier divided by the closed loop voltage gain (i.e. the voltage gain set using R2 and R3). Even for the inexpensive μA741C the gain bandwidth product is 1MHz, which means that it provides a bandwidth of 10 to 100kHz at voltage gains from 100 to 10 times. This is far more than is really needed in many applications.

The excess bandwidth does not matter, but it can be beneficial to reduce the bandwidth if noise is proving to be problematic. The easiest way to do this is to add a filter capacitor in parallel with R2. This gives increased feedback at high frequencies, and rolls-off the amplifier's frequency response. In many applications the rate at which readings are taken is quite slow, and the rate at which input voltages changes is even slower. This permits quite a larger filter capacitor to be used, possibly giving a bandwidth of less than 1Hz. This would give a substantial reduction in the noise level.

Current Measurement

In theory it is quite easy to measure current using a computer plus an analogue to digital converter. The basic method used is shown in Figure 2.5. This really just consists of a resistor added across the input of the converter. The current flow through the resistor is proportional to the applied voltage, and readings from the converter are therefore easily converted into corresponding current flows.

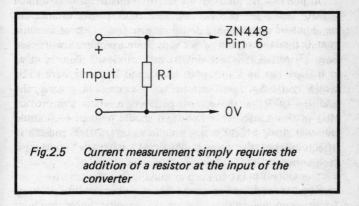

Fig.2.5   Current measurement simply requires the addition of a resistor at the input of the converter

For example, if R1 is given a value of 1k, a full scale potential of 2.55 volts will result from a current flow of 2.55 milliamps (2.55 volts divided by 1000 ohms = 0.00255 amps, or 2.55 milliamps). Readings from the converter can therefore be converted into milliamps simply by dividing them by 100. The table on page 38 shows the resistor values required for some useful full scale currents.

Higher values will give greater sensitivity, but the input resistance of the converter could significantly shunt the input

Resistance	Full Scale Current
1R	2.55 amps
10R	255 milliamps
100R	25.5 milliamps
1k	2.55 milliamps
10k	255 microamps

resistor, giving poor accuracy. An input buffer amplifier would be needed to avoid this problem. Note that values such as 1R, 10R, etc., give readings from the converter that are easily converted into current readings. Values such as 4k7, 22R, etc., are usable, but would be inconvenient in practice. You could easily find yourself with a system that measures currents in increments such as 1.563 milliamps!

Although this method of current measurement is fine in theory, there are one or two important points to keep in mind when using such a setup in practice. One of these is simply that the adding of R1 into the current path will often have a significant effect on the current flow. Bear in mind that there can be a voltage drop of up to 2.55 volts across R1, which could be significant in many cases. In general, the addition of R1 in the current path will result in some reduction in the current that flows. It should perhaps be pointed out that this problem is not unique to this system, and it also affects all but the most sophisticated of current measuring techniques.

The second point to keep in mind is that the negative input terminal is connected to earth. This is not normally a problem when measuring voltages, where it is usually the voltage with respect to earth that must be measured. With current measurement though, it is often necessary to measure currents where neither input terminal will be at earth potential. This circuit is unsuitable for measurements of this type.

Temperature Measurement
There are numerous sensors which can be used for temperature measurement. These range from a humble silicon diode to exotic (and expensive) sensors which can respond almost

instantly to temperature changes. For most purposes an integrated circuit temperature sensor is the best option. These are basically a diode sensor plus some signal processing circuitry which gives an output voltage that relates easily to the sensed temperature.

A silicon diode is forward biased for operation as a temperature sensor. The voltage across a forward biased silicon junction is about 0.65 volts, but the precise voltage is dependent on several factors. The two main ones are the bias current used, and the temperature. If the diode is fed from a constant current source, and a low current is used in order to avoid self-heating, the bias voltage is dependent on the ambient temperature. The voltage does not change much with variations in the applied temperature, and there is typically a drop of about two or three millivolts for each increase in temperature by one degree Celsius. The linearity is very good though, and some simple level shifter and amplifier circuitry is all that is needed in order to provide a more useful output voltage range.

There are a number of integrated circuit temperature sensors available, but for use with a computer via an analogue-to-digital converter the LM35 series of devices are the best choices for most applications. They were probably designed primarily for use in temperature sensor probes for digital multimeters, but computer temperature sensing places almost identical requirements on the sensor.

The output from an LM35 is equal to 0.01 volts (10 millivolts) per degree Celsius. It will operate over a supply voltage range of 4 volts to 30 volts. The typical current consumption of just 56 microamps ensures that there is a very low level of self-heating, especially when the device is operated from a low voltage supply. The LM35DZ operates over a temperature range of 0 to 100 degrees Celsius, and the LM35CZ operates over a range of −40 to 110 degrees Celsius.

On the face of it the LM35 is an ideal companion to a ZN448 series analogue-to-digital converter. The output of 10 millivolts per degree Celsius matches the resolution of the ZN448 converters. Simply feeding the output of the LM35 to the input of a ZN448 gives readings from the converter that are directly in degrees Celsius.

In practice things are not quite as simple as this. Such a system would work perfectly well, but would provide a resolution of just one degree Celsius. This is not really very good, and would be totally inadequate for many practical purposes. In order to fully exploit a system which utilizes an analogue-to-digital converter the voltage range provided by the signal source must be something approaching the input voltage range of the converter. In this case a 0 to 100 degree input temperature range would give an output voltage range of 0 to 1 volt. This would result in the maximum input voltage to the converter never reaching half the full scale potential. In effect, the converter is relegated from 8 bit to 7 bit resolution.

Better results are obtained if the output of the temperature sensor is amplified, so that the output voltage range comes closer to fully driving the converter. Figure 2.6 shows the circuit diagram for a simple temperature sensor of this type.

IC1 is the LM35 temperature sensor, and the only discrete component this requires is R1. Even R1 can be omitted if operation at low temperatures (about 2 degrees Celsius or less) is not required. If operation up to 100 degrees is satisfactory, use an LM35DZ for IC1. An LM35CZ must be used if operation up to 110 degrees Celsius is required.

IC2 is the amplifier, and this is an operational amplifier used in the non-inverting mode. VR2 is adjusted to give a voltage amplification of two times, which gives an output voltage of 20 millivolts per degree Celsius. In order to convert readings into degrees Celsius it is therefore necessary to divide them by two. This boosts the resolution of the system to a more useful 0.5 degrees Celsius. VR1 is an offset null control which is used to ensure accurate results at low temperature readings.

It is normal with this type of equipment for the temperature sensor to be fitted into some sort of probe assembly. Apart from making everything much neater, this also protects IC1, and the connections to it, from moisture in the air, etc. Note that some sort of protective casing is essential if the sensor is to be used in liquids. In addition to protecting IC1 from the liquid, this is also necessary to prevent signals from IC1's leadouts passing through the liquid. This would upset the operation of the circuit, and due to an electrolytic action

40

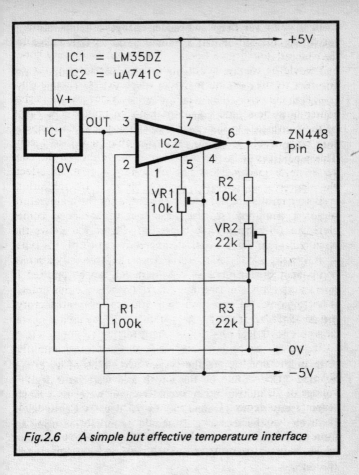

Fig.2.6 A simple but effective temperature interface

it could also alter any liquid into which IC1 was placed.

A small glass test tube makes a good basis for a probe. In order to speed up the response time of the sensor it is a good idea to use some silicone grease to provide a good thermal contact between IC1 and the test tube. Note though, that even with some silicone grease included in the probe assembly, the response time of the sensor will still not be very fast. It can take several seconds for the sensor to adjust to temperature changes. With very large and sudden changes in temperature it could take the sensor half a minute or so to fully adjust to the changes.

This short program is suitable for use with the temperature interface. It is basically the same as the voltage reading program, but one or two changes are required. The main one is a division by two rather than 50 at line 50. Readings are also taken at a slightly slower rate. Taking them at a higher rate is pointless in this case, due to the fairly slow response time of the temperature probe.

```
10  REM temperature reading program
20  CLS
30  OUT 768,0
40  X = INP(768)
50  X = X/2
60  CLS
70  PRINT X"Degrees Centigrade"
80  FOR D = 1 TO 10000
90  NEXT D
100 A$ = INKEY$
110 IF LEN(A$) = 0 THEN GOTO 30
```

In order to calcibrate the system two glasses of water are required. One should be filled with iced water at 0 degrees Centigrade, while the other should contain water at a much higher temperature (around 50 to 70 degrees Centigrade). The water in the second glass should be monitored using an accurate thermometer so that you always know its precise temperature. Initially VR1 and VR2 should be set at roughly mid settings.

First place the sensor in the cold water and wait for the sensor to adjust to the low temperature. If a reading of more than zero is not being obtained, adjust VR1 for such a reading. Then carefully adjust VR1 just far enough to reduce the reading to zero. Next place the sensor in the hot water and again wait for it to settle down at the new temperature. VR2 is then adjusted for the correct reading, after noting the precise temperature of the water as indicated on the calibration thermometer. Repeat this procedure once or twice to make sure that everything is setup accurately. The system is then ready for use.

Other Ranges

In some applications it will not be necessary to measure temperatures as high as 100 degrees Centigrade, or anything approaching this figure. For example, if the unit is used to monitor the outside air temperature it is unlikely that the maximum reading would ever exceed 50 degrees Centigrade. In such cases it is better to use a restricted temperature range so that better use is made of the available resolution.

A 0 to 50 degree temperature range could be accommodated using a gain of five times in the d.c. amplifier. The 0 to 0.5 volt output of the sensor would then be boosted to 0 to 2.5 volts, which is obviously within the 2.55 volt maximum of the converter. This would give an improved resolution of 0.2 degrees Centigrade, and dividing readings from the converter by five would give readings in degrees Centigrade. The only modification needed to the circuit in order to give this modified temperature range is to increase R2 from 10k to 75k. The setting up procedure remains the same as before.

The LM35CZ can handle negative temperatures down to −40 degrees Centigrade, but these provide negative output voltages. The ZN448 series of converters are unable to handle negative input voltages, and negative temperatures can only be accommodated if some level shifting is used. Some simple mathematics in the software can then be used to give appropriate temperature readings.

The most simple method of level shifting is to use the offset null control (VR1) to deliberately introduce a specific offset, rather than simply using it to eliminate any offset that might be present. For example, with the sensor at −10 degrees Centigrade, VR1 can be adjusted for a reading of zero from the converter. With the sensor then at (say) 45 degrees, VR2 would be adjusted for a reading of 110 from the converter (55 degrees). Of course, the software would have to be altered to suit the 10 degree offset. Thus, instead of simply dividing values read from the converter by two, it would also be necessary to deduct 10 degrees. These readings of zero and

55 would then be brought down to the correct temperatures of −10 and 45 degrees Celsius.

This is a rather crude way of handling things, but it seems to work quite well in practice. It would probably be possible to use larger offsets so that lower temperatures could be accommodated, but I have not tried this in practice due to the lack of suitably low calibration temperatures.

Resistance

Resistance can be measured using a method which is similar to the one for current measurement which was described previously. However, rather than using a fixed resistor and a variable current, it is the current that is constant and the resistance which changes. As a simple example, assume that the input of the converter is fed from a constant current generator circuit which provides an output current of 1 milliamp. With a 1k test resistor it would require 1 volt to give the 1 milliamp current flow (1000 ohms multiplied by 0.001 amps equals 1 volt). A 2k test resistor would produce an input to the converter of 2 volts (2000 ohms multiplied by 0.001 amps equals 2 volts).

It should be apparent from this that, provided a sensible current level is chosen, there is no difficulty in converting readings from the converter into corresponding resistance readings. In this example it is merely necessary to multiply by ten in order to produce readings in ohms, or to divide by 100 in order to give readings in kilohms. This table shows some test currents and the full scale resistance ranges that they provide.

Current	Full Scale Resistance
10mA	255R
1mA	2.55k
100μA	25.5k
10μA	255k
1μA	2.55M
0.1μA	25.5M

Figure 2.7 shows the circuit diagram for a resistance meter circuit that is based on the system outlined here. TR1 operates

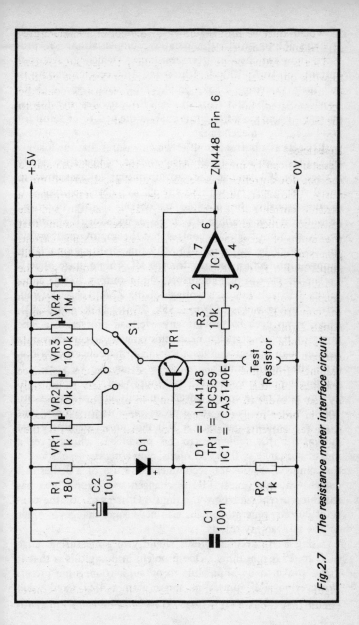

Fig.2.7   The resistance meter interface circuit

45

in a conventional constant current generator circuit, which includes D1 to provide temperature compensation. S1 provides four switched emitter resistances, which give output currents of 1mA, 100μA, 10μA, and 1μA (corresponding to full scale values of 2.55k, 25.5k, 255k, and 2.55M). VR1 provides the highest current − VR4 provides the lowest current. Using preset resistors enables the unit to be setup for good accuracy on each range.

IC1 acts as a buffer amplifier which ensures that the loading on the test resistor is totally insignificant. No negative supply is used for IC1, and it will provide output voltages down to the 0 volt supply rail without the aid of a negative supply. It would probably be possible to obtain slightly improved accuracy at low readings if IC1 was provided with a negative supply and an offset null control, but the improvement would probably not be sufficient to justify this modification. R3 is simply a protection resistor for the MOS input stage of IC1.

The circuit will just about provide an output voltage equal to the 2.55 volt full scale voltage of the ZN448 series of converters, giving ranges of 0 to 2.55k, 25.5k, 255k, and 2.55M. There is no need to provide any overload protection at the input of the converter, because this circuit can not provide a high enough output voltage to damage the converter. However, the circuit must be powered from the PC's +5 volt supply, and not from the +12 volt supply rail.

This four range circuit covers a useful range of resistances, but it is possible to use more preset resistors to give the unit further measuring ranges. A 100-ohm preset permits a test current of 10 milliamps to be produced, which gives a measuring range of 0 to 255 ohms, increasing the resolution to one ohm. I would not recommend the use of a higher test current though, unless TR1 is changed to a type which has suitable current and power ratings. Other parts of the constant current generator might also need some changes in order to give satisfactory results.

Using a 10-megohm preset would give a measuring range of 0 to 25.5 megohms. One problem in doing this is that it might prove to be impossible to obtain a 10-megohm preset. However, a 4M7 preset in series with a 4M7 fixed value resistor should be satisfactory. A second problem is that with a maximum collector current of just 0.1 microamps TR1 can not be expected to operate very efficiently. Good accuracy might be obtained, but any slight leakage current through TR1 could easily cause a significant loss of linearity. Therefore, I can not guarantee that good results will be obtained on a 25.5-megohm range.

Software

The software for this device presents no major difficulty. It is just a matter of doing some simple mathematics to suit the range in use, and displaying "kilohms", or "megohms" after the value printed on the screen. For example, on the 0 to 25.5k range the value returned from the converter must be divided by 10 to give an answer in kilohms, and the word "kilohms" or just "k" should obviously be displayed after the value.

It is a good idea to include a routine that will detect a returned value of 255 and display an "Overload" warning on the screen. A value of 255 does not necessarily mean that the input voltage to the converter has gone beyond the full scale value, but in most cases this will be what has happened, and an overload has to be assumed. Note that with no resistor connected to the circuit a reading of 255 will be returned from the converter.

This simple GW BASIC program provides the bare necessities for a resistance meter program. Lines 30 and 40 set variables Y and B$ at their initial values of 100 and "k". Y is the number by which the returned values are divided, and this is either 1, 10, or 100, depending on the range in use. B$ is the units indicator, which is either "k" or "M" (or "kilohms" and "megohms" if you prefer). The initial values provide operation on range 1 (0 to 2.55k).

In order to change range the numeric keys from "1" to "4" are used. Pressing a key selects the appropriate range (e.g. pressing the "3" key selects range 3, which measures from 0 to 255k). A key press is detected by lines 70 and 80, which then take the program to a subroutine. The subroutine uses a series of IF . . . . THEN statements to detect which key has been pressed, and to make any necessary changes to variables X and B$. The program then loops normally, taking and displaying readings on the screen until another key is pressed. The program can be terminated by pressing the "5" key. This is detected by line 230 of the subroutine, which then halts the program with an END instruction.

```
10  REM resistance meter program
20  CLS
30  Y = 100
40  B$ = "k"
50  OUT 768,0
60  X = INP(768)
70  A$ = INKEY$
80  IF LEN(A$) = 1 THEN GOSUB 150
90  CLS
100 IF X = 255 THEN PRINT "POSSI
BLE OVERLOAD!"
110 PRINT X/Y B$
120 FOR D = 1 TO 5000
130 NEXT D
140 GOTO 50
150 IF ASC(A$) = 49 THEN Y = 100
160 IF ASC(A$) = 49 THEN B$ =
"k"
170 IF ASC(A$) = 50 THEN Y = 10
180 IF ASC(A$) = 50 THEN B$ =
"k"
190 IF ASC(A$) = 51 THEN Y = 1
200 IF ASC(A$) = 51 THEN B$ =
"k"
210 IF ASC(A$) = 52 THEN Y = 100
220 IF ASC(A$) = 52 THEN B$ =
"M"
230 IF ASC(A$) = 53 THEN END
240 RETURN
```

Calibration

In order to calibrate the unit four precision resistors (a tolerance of 1% or better) are required. These should have values that are close to the full scale values of the four ranges.

48

Resistors of 2k2, 22k, 220k, and 2M2 in value are good choices. Start with all four presets at approximately two-thirds of maximum resistance. Switch the unit to the 2.55k range and connect the 2k2 calibration resistor to the input terminals. Then adjust VR1 for a reading of 2.20 kilohms. Repeat the same basic procedure on the other three ranges using the 22k, 220k, and 2M2 calibration resistors. The unit is then ready for use.

Remember that the unit must be switched to a suitable range, and that there must be some means of telling the software which range is in use. It is not difficult to implement automatic range sensing if some spare digital inputs are available. The most simple method of providing this automatic sensing is to have an extra pole on the range switch. This can be used to drive four digital inputs in the manner shown in Figure 2.8. A software routine can read the inputs, and determine which range is in use by detecting which of the inputs has been taken high.

Components for Figure 2.7

Resistors (all 0.25 watt 5% carbon film)
R1   180R
R2   1k
R3   10k

Potentiometers
VR1   1k miniature preset
VR2   10k miniature preset
VR3   100k miniature preset
VR4   1M miniature preset

Capacitors
C1   100n ceramic
C2 10μ 25V elect

Semiconductors
IC1   CA3140E
TR1   BC559
D1   1N4148

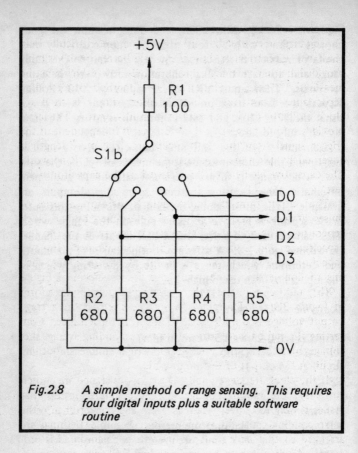

Fig.2.8   A simple method of range sensing. This requires four digital inputs plus a suitable software routine

Miscellaneous

S1   4-way 3-pole rotary switch (only one pole used)

8-pin d.i.l. holder

Test sockets and leads (e.g. 1mm sockets and plugs plus crocodile clips)

Case, circuit board, control knob, etc.

50

Capacitance Measurement

Capacitance measurement is slightly more difficult than resistance measurement, but it can still be reasonably simple provided neither very high nor extremely low values must be measured. There is more than one method of providing capacitance measurement, but the most simple is to use a clock oscillator driving a monostable multivibrator. The latter provides output pulses of a duration that is independent of the trigger signal from the clock oscillator. The pulse length is governed by the time constant of a simple C − R network. The capacitive element of this network is the capacitor under test.

The output from the monostable is therefore a series of pulses at a constant rate which is determined by the clock generator. The width of the pulses is governed by the test capacitance, and is proportional to the capacitance. If a test capacitor gave the output waveform of Figure 2.9(a), then one of double that value would give the waveform of Figure 2.9(b), and one four times that value would give the waveform of Figure 2.9(c). The point to note here is that the average output voltage is proportional to the test capacitance. Converting the pulsed waveform into a corresponding average d.c. voltage merely requires the addition of a simple smoothing circuit at the output of the monostable.

If the clock frequency and the timing resistance are chosen correctly, the output voltage will have a relationship that makes it easy to convert readings from the converter into the corresponding capacitance values. For example, if things are arranged so that an output of one volt per nanofarad is produced, dividing values by one hundred will give readings in nanofarads, or multiplying by ten will give readings in picofarads.

Figure 2.10 shows the circuit diagram for a capacitance meter interface that is suitable for operation with a ZN448 series converter. The clock oscillator uses IC1 in the standard 555 astable (oscillator) mode. VR1 enables some variation in the operating frequency, and this is needed for calibration purposes.

The monostable is based on IC2, which is another 555 timer. This type of monostable can only provide output

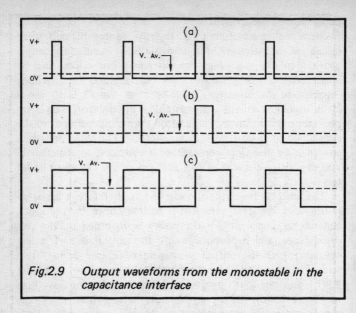

Fig.2.9 *Output waveforms from the monostable in the capacitance interface*

pulses that are longer than the input pulses — not shorter. This is potentially a fatal flaw in the current context, but this problem is overcome by using a clock oscillator circuit that generates very short negative output pulses. This is achieved by giving R2 a value which is low in comparison to the series resistance of R1 and VR1, so that C2's discharge time is kept very short.

A low power version of the 555 is specified for IC1 and IC2, and there are two reasons for this. One is that the minimum pulse duration from a low power 555 is shorter than that from a standard 555. This avoids problems with poor accuracy at low readings due to d.c. offsets on the output voltage. The other is that a low power 555 seems to have less than half the self-capacitance of an ordinary 555, which gives better accuracy when measuring small capacitances. Although the TLC555CP is specified for IC1 and IC2, the ICM7555 also seems to give satisfactory results.

IC2 has four switched timing resistors, giving four measuring ranges. R6 to R3 respectively give full scale values of

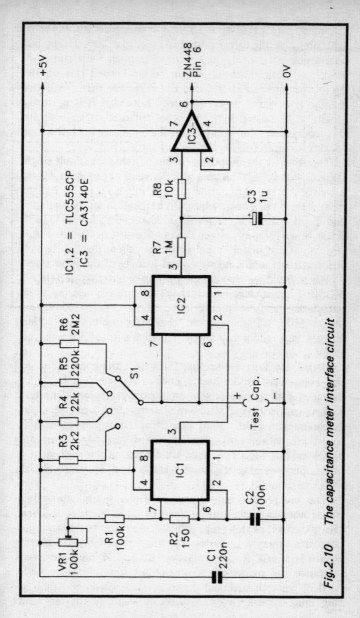

Fig.2.10   The capacitance meter interface circuit

53

2.55n, 25.5n, 255n, and 2.55μ. A timing resistor value of 220 ohms would give a further range of 0 to 25.5μ, but would give a relatively high current through the timing network. I noticed no ill effects when I tried this on the prototype interface, but I can not guarantee that it will give satisfactory results in every case. Note that it is perfectly alright to test electrolytics or other polarised capacitors with this equipment, but they must be connected to the test sockets with the polarity shown in Figure 2.10.

The filter at the output of the monostable is a simple single stage C − R type. The long time constant of one second gives a well smoothed d.c. output voltage, but it results in a slight delay before the circuit adjusts to a change in test capacitance and displays an accurate reading. Always wait for readings to settle down properly when taking measurements using this system. IC3 is merely a unity voltage gain buffer stage which ensures that there is no significant loading of the filter stage.

When building the circuit bear in mind that IC3 has a MOSFET input stage, and that it therefore requires the usual anti-static handling precautions. Low power 555 timers utilize MOS technology, but they have built-in protection circuits that render any special handling precautions unnecessary.

Avoid any long connecting leads from the main circuit to the component under test. Long leads here are likely to degrade accuracy, especially on the lowest range. The test sockets can be a pair of one millimetre sockets spaced about 10 millimetres apart. Many capacitors can be plugged straight into these without any problems. For "awkward" components a pair of short test leads are needed. These each have a one millimetre plug at one end and a small crocodile clip at the other.

The circuit can be calibrated on any range, although I would not recommend using the 0 to 2.55n range for calibration purposes, as this range is likely to be slightly less accurate than the others. In order to obtain reasonably consistent accuracy across the four ranges, R3 to R6 must be close tolerance (1% or better) resistors. A calibration capacitor is needed, and this should have a value which is equal to something approaching the full scale value of the range on which the unit is to be calibrated.

For this example we will assume that the unit is to be calibrated on the 0 to 25.5n range, and that a 22n calibration component is to be used. Set S1 to the appropriate range, set VR1 at a roughly mid setting, and then connect the calibration capacitor across the input sockets. VR1 is then adjusted for a reading of 22.0n. It can be a little tricky to get the adjustment spot-on due to a slight sluggishness in the unit to respond to changes in VR1's setting. This is due to the long time constant of the filter stage. However, if VR1 is adjusted slowly and carefully it is not too difficult to find the correct setting.

It must be pointed out that a capacitor which has an excessive value for the range in use can actually provide an in-range reading. What happens here is that the output pulses from IC2 become very long, so that the monostable only triggers on (say) every other clock cycle. This can result in an output voltage as low as half the supply voltage, or 2.5 volts in this case. Clearly this is within the 2.55 volt full range potential of the converter. The easiest way of avoiding erroneous results is to have values above 240 produce an overload warning. An input voltage to the converter of under 2.4 volts is then needed to give an in-range reading. This can not occur with a capacitor that has an excessive reading even if the actual supply voltage is fractionally lower than the nominal 5-volt level.

The GW BASIC listing on page 56 is for use with the capacitance meter interface, and it follows along much the same basic lines as the resistance meter program.

Components for Figure 2.10

Resistors

R1	100k 5% carbon film
R2	150R 5% carbon film
R3	2k2 1% metal film
R4	22k 1% metal film
R5	220k 1% metal film
R6	2M2 1% metal film
R7	1M 5% carbon film
R8	10k 5% carbon film

```
10  REM capacitance meter program
20  CLS
30  Y = 100
40  B$ = "n"
50  OUT 768,0
60  X = INP(768)
70  A$ = INKEY$
80  IF LEN(A$) = 1 THEN GOSUB 150
90  CLS
100 IF X > 240 THEN PRINT "POSSI
BLE OVERLOAD!"
110 PRINT X/Y B$
120 FOR D = 1 TO 5000
130 NEXT D
140 GOTO 50
150 IF ASC(A$) = 49 THEN Y = 100
160 IF ASC(A$) = 49 THEN B$ =
"n"
170 IF ASC(A$) = 50 THEN Y = 10
180 IF ASC(A$) = 50 THEN B$ =
"n"
190 IF ASC(A$) = 51 THEN Y = 1
200 IF ASC(A$) = 51 THEN B$ =
"n"
210 IF ASC(A$) = 52 THEN Y = 100
220 IF ASC(A$) = 52 THEN B$ =
"u"
230 IF ASC(A$) = 53 THEN END
240 RETURN
```

Potentiometer

VR1	100k preset

Capacitors

C1	220n ceramic
C2	100n polyester
C3	1μ 63V elect

Semiconductors

IC1	TLC555CP (see text)

| IC2 | TLC555CP (see text) |
| IC3 | CA3140E |

Miscellaneous

S1	4-way 3-pole rotary switch (only one pole used)
	8-pin d.i.l. holder (3 off)
	Test sockets and leads (e.g. 1mm sockets and plugs plus crocodile clips)
	Case, circuit board, control knob, etc.

Position Sensing

Amongst other things, the next chapter deals with the computer control of small electric motors. When controlling model trains, robot arms, etc., it is often necessary to have some form of feedback from the device being controlled if proper automatic control is to be achieved. For example, it is quite easy to have a model train controller that is computer controlled, with the train stopping and starting without the need for any human intervention. However, in its most basic form this results in the train stopping and starting at random positions on the track. The results obtained do not really justify the effort involved. With the aid of a simple feedback mechanism the train can be made to stop and start at any desired point (or points) on the track, giving much more pleasing results.

In general, the more sophisticated the feedback to the controller, the greater the accuracy that can be achieved in any control application. In our model train example, a single sensor could detect the train some way ahead of the station. The train could then be automatically decelerated and made to stop at the station. The problem with this type of thing is in getting consistent results, with the train always stopping exactly at the right place. Provided the train was always travelling at the same speed as it passed the sensor, with some trial and error it would probably be possible to get the train to stop in more or less the same place each time. This simple setup might provide adequate accuracy, or it might not. The only way to find out would be to try it in practice. In my experience a simple setup of this type usually falls just short of providing acceptable results.

If the train was not always travelling at the same speed as it passed the sensor (which is likely to be the case in practice), the chances of success would be very small. In theory it would be possible to have a suitable deceleration rate precalculated for each possible speed, but in practice the chances of implementing such a system successfully are remote. The time involved in getting everything just right would be enormous, and the degree of accuracy obtained would fall some way short of being acceptable.

A better way of handling things is to have two sensors. As before, one would be some way ahead of the station, and on passing this one the train would be made to delecerate. However, it would not be brought to a complete halt. Instead, after the deceleration phase the train would be made to keep moving very slowly. The second sensor would be positioned in the station, and the train would be brought to a halt as it passed this sensor. In this way very precise positioning of the train can be achieved. Furthermore, it can be achieved very easily, which makes the addition of the second sensor very worthwhile indeed.

Further sensors could be added ahead of the station so that the deceleration of the train could be controlled very accurately, and greater realism could be achieved. This is something where the laws of diminishing returns come into play though. Adding one sensor gives a tremendous improvement to the system. Adding a second one also brings great benefits, making it much easier to obtain an adequate degree of accuracy, as well as giving much greater precision. Adding further sensors does permit improved results to be obtained, but the improvement is less obvious. With each sensor that is added, the improvement it provides is that much less than that provided by its predecessor. Whether or not it is worth using more than two sensors really depends on how much of a perfectionist you happen to be.

Reed Switches

A micro-switch is the simplest and most convenient form of sensor for robotics and some other applications. A micro-switch is basically just an ordinary switch, but instead of having manual operation via a push-button, slider knob, or whatever, it has some sort of lever mechanism that is operated automatically. For example, a micro-switch could be positioned such that it is operated when a robot arm is moved round to a certain position. A micro-switch can be used as a model train sensor if the lever can be positioned where it will be activated by the passing train. In practice it is often difficult to obtain reliable results using this method, and if you get things slightly wrong there can be frequent derailments!

A reed switch is a more popular method of sensing for model train applications. A reed switch is basically just two small pieces of springy metal that overlap one another, as in Figure 2.11. These pieces of metal are the "reeds", and they are normally fitted in a glass envelope. The reeds are spaced

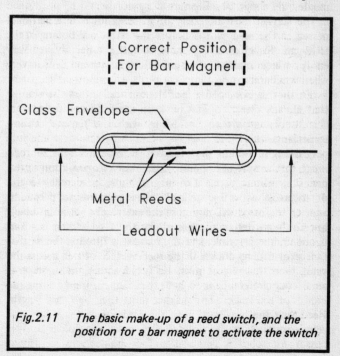

Fig.2.11   The basic make-up of a reed switch, and the
position for a bar magnet to activate the switch

slightly apart so that they are not quite in electrical contact with each other. If you look carefully at one of these switches you should be able to see the reeds and the gap through the glass casing.

If a reasonably strong bar magnet is placed next to a reed switch, the two reeds become temporarily magnetised by the field of the magnet. The two ends of the reeds that are in close proximity to each other have opposite poles, and accordingly they are attracted to one another. Due to the flexible nature of the reeds, this results in the overlapping ends moving together and touching, so that electrical contact is completed. This gives a simple switching action, with the switch open when the magnet is absent, and closed when it is brought close to the reeds. The contact ratings of reed switches are very low incidentally, but they are more than adequate for position sensing, where they will typically handle only about 10 milliamps at 5 volts d.c.

The magnet must normally be within about 20 to 30 millimetres of the reed switch before the latter will be activated. Although this gives a very short operating range, it is sufficient for use in computerised model train systems, and many other computer control applications. An important factor in favour of this system for model train use is that there is no need for any direct contact between the train and the sensor. This totally avoids any problems with the sensors causing derailments.

Positioning of the bar magnet is crucial, and the reed switch will simply not operate if the relative orientation of the magnet is not correct. The magnet must be parallel to the switch, as shown in Figure 2.11. Having the magnet perpendicular to the reeds will not close the switch even at point-blank range. In model train applications the reed switch is often placed under the track, and the magnet is fitted in the base of a piece of rolling stock. If the reed switch is fitted across the track, then the magnet must be fitted across the carriage or truck. My preference is to have the magnet running along the middle of the track. The magnet must then be fitted lengthwise along the base section of the piece of rolling stock, and not across it.

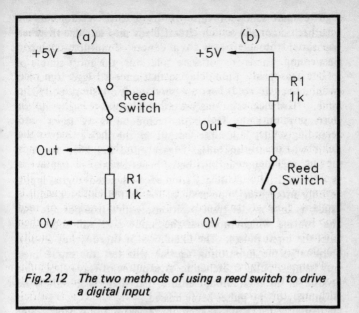

Fig.2.12 *The two methods of using a reed switch to drive a digital input*

Figure 2.12 shows the two basic methods of using a reed switch (or any other mechanical switch) to drive a digital input of a computer. The difference between the two is that the output of (a) is normally low and goes high when the switch is activated, while the output of (b) is normally high and goes low when the switch is activated. In a computer application it does not normally matter which method of connection is used, as the software can be written to suit either method. My preference is for the method shown in (a), as it is easier to think in terms of a returned value of 0 as the standby state, and a returned value of 1, 2, etc. as the active state.

Although this type of sensor may seem to be so simple that nothing could go wrong in practice, there are a few potential problems. Mechanical switches are notoriously noisy, and often suffer from a certain amount of contact bounce. This results in a series of brief pulses being produced each time the switch opens or closes, rather than single "clean" transitions being produced.

The importance of this (or the lack of it) depends on whether or not the switch circuit feeds into an edge triggered input. If it does, there is a real danger of multiple triggering occurring. There are software solutions, the most simple of which is to have a time delay so that once a trigger signal has been detected, no others are serviced for a short period of time. Hardware solutions are more popular though, and are extremely simple. The basic technique is to use a pulse stretcher which holds the output in the active state for a short while once an initial trigger pulse has been received.

This technique can also be of benefit if the switch circuit is used to drive an ordinary (non-edge triggered) digital input. If only momentary operation of the switch will be produced (such as in a model train position sensor), it is possible that the routine which monitors the input port will sometimes miss the input pulses. The likelihood of this depends on how frequently the monitoring routine will test the input lines, but using a pulse stretcher to give pulses of (say) about one second in duration should ensure that there is absolutely no possibility of any pulses being missed.

Figure 2.13 shows the circuit diagram for a very simple pulse stretcher based on a trigger/inverter stage. The latter could be one of the six trigger/inverters in a 74LS14. This

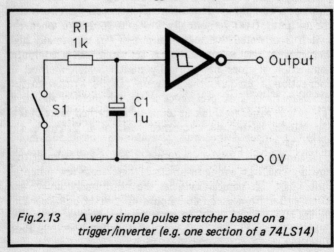

Fig.2.13   A very simple pulse stretcher based on a
            trigger/inverter (e.g. one section of a 74LS14)

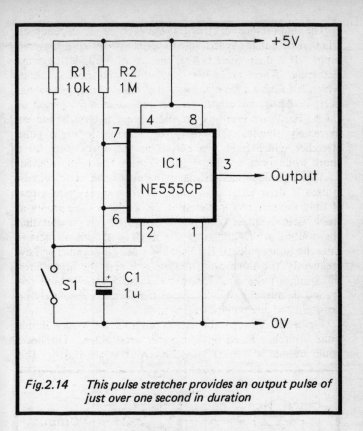

Fig.2.14   This pulse stretcher provides an output pulse of just over one second in duration

does not provide a particularly long output pulse, but it is usually sufficient to provide effective de-bouncing. It is very economic since six resistors, six capacitors, and one 74LS14 will provide half a dozen de-bounce circuits.

For a longer output pulse duration the basic 555 monostable circuit of Figure 2.14 can be used. R2 and C1 are the timing components, and the pulse duration is equal to 1.1 C R seconds (where C is the timing capacitor value in microfarads, and R is the timing resistance in megohms). The specified values give a pulse duration of about 1.1 seconds, but using larger timing component values it is possible to obtain pulse durations of several seconds if necessary.

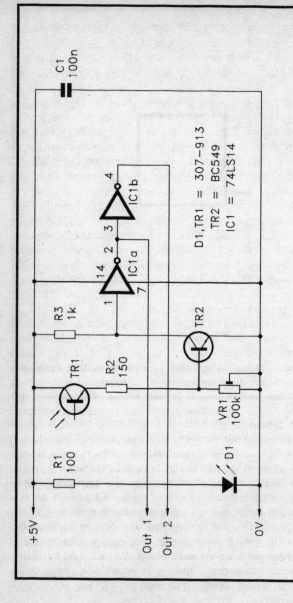

Fig.2.15   An optical sensor using a reflective opto-sensor device (DI-TR1)

C1
100n

4
IC1b

14   2   3
IC1a
1   7

R3
1k

TR1

R2
150

TR2

R1
100

D1

VR1
100k

+5V

Out 1
Out 2

0V

D1,TR1 = 307-913
TR2 = BC549
IC1 = 74LS14

64

Opto Sensor

If you would prefer to use a more modern method of sensing, an optical sensor is a good choice. The circuit of Figure 2.15 is based on a reflective opto-sensor, which is basically just an infra-red l.e.d. and a photo-transistor in the same case, and "looking" in the same direction. The sensor I used is the RS "standard" type (the type number given in Figure 2.15 is actually the RS/Electromail order code, with no type number being given for this device in the catalogues). The circuit will also work with the RS "miniature" reflective opto-sensor, or the Maplin OPB706B (which seems to be identical to the RS "miniature" type). However, the miniature type seems to give slightly lower sensitivity than the "standard" size sensor.

The basic idea of a reflective opt-sensor is to have the l.e.d. transmit a constant beam of infra-red "light". The photo-transistor picks up any of the infra-red signal that is reflected back to the sensor. The l.e.d. section of the sensor is simply fed with a forward bias current via current limiting resistor R1. The latter sets the l.e.d. current at 30 milliamps, which is high enough to give good results, but is comfortably within the 40 milliamp maximum rating of the l.e.d.

Even if the object to be detected is fairly reflective, it must be very close to the sensor in order to give enough infra-red signal on the photo-transistor to fully turn it on. Much improved range can be obtained if, as in this circuit, the photo-transistor drives an amplifier stage. The amplifier is a basic common emitter switch based on TR2. VR1 permits the sensitivity of the circuit to be controlled (maximum resistance giving maximum sensitivity).

The output from TR2 may not always switch cleanly and rapidly from one logic level to the other. In fact the voltage here can hover at illegal voltages between the valid logic 0 and logic 1 potentials. Therefore, the output from TR2 is fed to a couple of Schmitt trigger/inverter stages which give an output that will be at one logic level or the other, apart from fast transitions from one state to the other. Output 1 is normally low and it goes high when an object is sensed. Output 2 is an inversion of this.

Note that Figure 2.15 correctly shows no connection to the base of TR1. In fact the base terminal of TR1 is not externally accessible, and it is therefore impossible to make a connection to it. If a long lead of more than about half a metre is used to connect the reflective sensor and the main circuit, I would recommend using a multi-way screened cable. The cathode terminal of D1 should connect to the screen of the cable.

A certain amount of thought needs to be used when setting up a sensor of this type. The object to be sensed must obviously be reasonably reflective, but most things seem to reflect rather more infra-red than you would expect. Accordingly, this will not usually be a problem. However, where necessary the object to be sensed must be fitted with something that will provide the sensor with a suitably reflective target.

This type of sensor can only operate if the normal background level of reflection is quite low. It might actually be possible to get the sensor to operate properly if there is a high level of reflection under standby conditions. It would then be a matter of setting things up so that the object to be sensed produced a reduction in the amount of reflected infra-red. It is certainly possible to do this under the right circumstances, but the normal method of operation is likely to provide better reliability, and is the one that should be used wherever possible.

It is essential to give VR1 a suitable setting if the sensor is to function reliably. This just means adjusting VR1 for highest resistance that does not result in the circuit being activated under standby conditions. An advantage of an optical sensor of this type over a reed switch is that it can provide a much greater range. Critical adjustment of VR1 may well provide an operating range of half a metre or more. In the interest of good reliability though, it is probably best to settle for an operating range of about 100 millimetres or less if the objects to be sensed are fairly small.

A drawback of this type of sensor in a model train context is that the passing train may well produce hundreds of output pulses from the sensor over a period of several seconds. A long pulse stretcher circuit could be used to combat this problem, but in this case my preference is for a software hold-off to prevent multiple triggering on each pass of the train.

Components for Figure 2.15

Resistors (all 0.25 watt 5% carbon film)
R1   100R
R2   150R
R3   1k

Potentiometer
VR1   100k miniature preset

Capacitor
C1   100n ceramic

Semiconductors
TR1/D1   307-913 standard reflective opto-switch
            (see text)
TR2   BC549
IC1   74LS14

Miscellaneous
14 pin d.i.l. i.c. holder
Case, circuit board, solder, etc.

Bitwise ANDing

There is a slight problem when reading sensor switches, in that you wish to know the state of just one line of an eight bit input port. The computer can only read all eight bits at once, and has no means of reading a selected bit. Some means of processing the returned value to mask off the other seven bits is needed. This would effectively be the same as only reading the bit that is of interest. The standard way of doing this is to use the bitwise AND function which is available in most PC languages (including GW BASIC).

Basically all you have to do is bitwise AND the value returned from the input port with the correct masking number. This number can be obtained from Table 1. For example, suppose that you wish to read a sensor switch connected to input line D3 of an input port. As you can see from Table 1, the correct masking number for bit 3 is 8. This simple GW BASIC program will read the input port at address 768, bitwise AND the returned value with a masking number of 8, and then print the answer on the screen.

```
10 REM masking program
20 X = INP(768)
30 X = X AND 8
40 PRINT X
```

The value printed on the screen is low if the relevant input is low, or the masking number (which is obviously 8 in this case) if it is high. In practice the ANDed value is used in a conditional instruction. For the sake of this example we will assume that the switch connected to D3 is a reed switch fitted to the track in a station. The program would therefore test the state of input line 3, and simply loop continuously while a value of 0 was returned. Once a value of 8 was detected, the program would then go to a routine that quickly brought the train to a halt.

Table 1

Input Line	Masking Number
0	1
1	2
2	4
3	8
4	16
5	32
6	64
7	128

Chapter 3

CONTROL PROJECTS

Controlling electronic and electrical equipment from a computer is often quite simple and straightforward. In particular, where simple on/off switching is required, the control circuit usually consists of just a latching digital output plus about three or four components. Variable control is a little more difficult, and requires a digital-to-analogue converter. However, for low voltage d.c. loads (e.g. model locomotives) the circuitry can still be kept quite simple.

A word of warning has to be given here, and this is simply that the necessary safety precautions must be taken when controlling any mains powered equipment. As explained later in this chapter, it is essential to have some form of isolation device between the computer and the controlled equipment. Without such isolation there will almost certainly be some blown fuses at switch-on, and the equipment could be very dangerous to touch. **Unless you are completely sure that you understand what you are doing, you should not attempt any project which involves the control of mains powered equipment (or any project which involves making connections to the mains supply wiring).**

Relay Control
A relay is just an ordinary mechanical switch that is operated via an electro-magnet. This may seem to be an out dated method of control in this computerised age, but a relay does have its advantages. One of these is simply that quite a modest input power permits massive power levels to be controlled, although I suppose that this is also true of many modern semiconductor power control devices. A relay though, provides this power control with the minimal losses associated with mechanical switches. The power loss through semiconductor power control devices is often not of great importance, but it tends to be a nuisance in that it results in a lot of heat being generated in the control device. Relays

provide control of high power loads without any need to bother with heatsinking.

Probably the main advantage of relays over other methods of control is the isolation that they provide. There is no direct connection between the electro-magnet and the switch contacts. This means that it is perfectly safe to control mains powered equipment via a relay. One proviso is that you must be careful to ensure that the input and output wiring to the relay are properly separated so that there is no risk of any accidental short circuits occurring here. Also, you need to carefully check the contact ratings of a relay to ensure that it can safely handle the voltage and current ratings involved in your particular application. This is something that applies whenever you use a relay, not just when it is being used in mains control applications. Note that the ratings of relay contacts are usually quite different for a.c. and d.c. loads (the d.c. ratings often being very much lower). Make sure that you check the set of ratings that are apposite to the type of power source you are using.

A relay driver can be very simple indeed, as can be seen from the relay driver circuit of Figure 3.1. This is basically just a transistor used as a common emitter switch. TR1 is biased into conduction when a logic 1 signal is applied to the input. This powers the relay coil and activates the switch contacts. The potential divider action across R1 and R2 ensures that TR1 is turned off with a logic 0 input level. The relay coil is then deactivated, and the switch contacts revert to their standby state. D1 is a protection diode which suppresses the high voltage spike which would otherwise be produced across the relay coil each time it was switched off. Although a coil resistance of 185 ohms is specified for the relay, the circuit will operate properly using any relay which has a 12-volt coil and a coil resistance of 185 ohms or more.

LEDs

The normal method of displaying information on a PC is, of course, via its display adapter and monitor. This is not always a good way of doing things, and is rather risky in situations where the system will be left unattended for long periods of time. Pieces of equipment such as television sets and computer

70

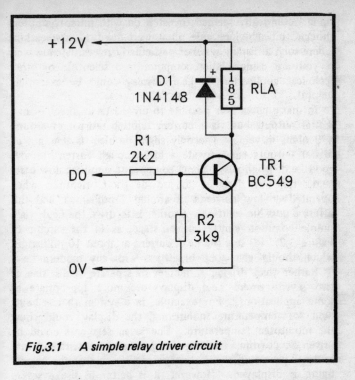

Fig.3.1   A simple relay driver circuit

monitors are considered to be a fire hazard if left unattended. Probably the best solution to the problem is to use some form of "solid state" screen, such as a liquid crystal type. However, this is likely to be a very costly solution.

A more practical solution is to opt for a simple status display of some sort. The monitor can then be switched off, with the status display providing some basic information to show that everything is functioning correctly. At its most basic a status display just consists of a flashing l.e.d. indicator to show that everything is functioning properly. More usually, there would be several l.e.d.s, showing what function or functions the computer was providing at that moment. At one time it was actually quite common for computer systems to have flashing l.e.d. displays which informed a suitably trained engineer exactly what the computer was up to. This type of thing never really seemed to catch on with microcomputers though, probably because they were used in applications where such a display was not particularly relevant. However, if you are using a microcomputer in a scientific or other technical application, a l.e.d. display could be extremely helpful.

In many cases it is possible to drive a l.e.d. direct from a digital output, but via a current limiting resistor of around 470 ohms in value. The only slight problem is that not all digital outputs can provide a high enough current to give good l.e.d. brightness. Some component suppliers now offer l.e.d.s that are designed to provide good brightness when operated at low currents of around 2 milliamps, and this offers a possible solution. Another is to drive the l.e.d. via a simple common emitter driver stage, as in the circuit of Figure 3.2. R3 sets the l.e.d. current at about 10 milliamps, which should give good brightness with any modern l.e.d.

Rather than driving a number of separate l.e.d.s, one or two seven-segment l.e.d displays are more appropriate to some applications. For example, in a system that is being used for temperature monitoring, the display could show the monitored temperature. The seven segments could be driven direct from a latching digital output port, with software routines providing the necessary decoding so that the correct figure is displayed. However, it is better to use a seven-segment decoder driver as this simplifies the software, and it requires fewer digital outputs per display. Only four outputs are required in order to drive a display via a b.c.d. (binary coded decimal) decoder.

Figure 3.3 shows the circuit diagram for a seven-segment driver circuit based on the CMOS 4511BE integrated circuit. Placing a latched binary number on the four data inputs produces the corresponding number on the display. For example, 0011 in binary is the equivalent of three in decimal, and so "3" will be produced on the display. If a value of more than nine is sent to IC1, the display will show non-standard characters (not numbers from 0 to 5 or the hexadecimal characters A to F).

It is quite in order to drive two digits from an eight-bit output port. The inputs of the extra circuit connect to D4 to

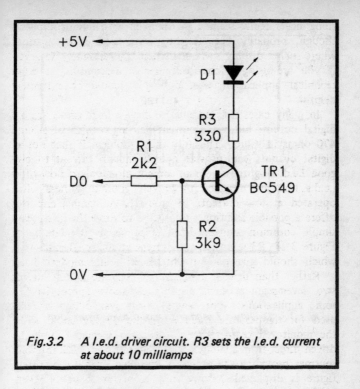

Fig.3.2   A l.e.d. driver circuit. R3 sets the l.e.d. current at about 10 milliamps

D7 instead of D0 to D3 (respectively). Remember that the value sent to the displays must be in binary coded decimal (b.c.d.) and not normal decimal. In order to get the right number displayed on both digits, the number for the most significant digit must be multiplied by 16. The number for the least significant digit is then added to this in order to give the final value written to the port. For instance, if "23" must be displayed, the most significant digit (2) must first be multiplied by 16. This obviously gives a value of 32, and the number for the least significant digit (3) is then added to the 32 to give a final answer of 35. It may seem strange to use a value of 35 to display "23" on the display, but binary and b.c.d. are decidedly different for decimal values above 9.

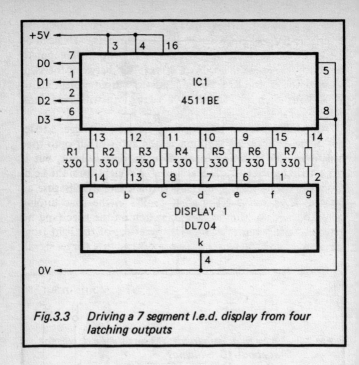

Fig.3.3   Driving a 7 segment l.e.d. display from four
          latching outputs

Solid-State Control

A relay is the traditional method of controlling mains loads from electronic equipment. There is an alternative in the form of a triac, which is a semiconductor switching device. The problem with using a triac is that it does not provide isolation from the mains supply, and is therefore unusable unless some form of isolation is included in the driver circuit. There are basically two options, which are a transformer and pulse generator circuit, or an opto-isolator. The latter is probably the more popular method, and is the one which would seem to be most appropriate in the current context.

An ordinary opto-isolator consists of a light emitting diode (l.e.d.) and a photo-transistor, both contained in an opaque casing. Normally the transistor only passes the minute leakage currents normally associated with silicon

74

devices. However, when the l.e.d. is activated it causes the transistor to pass much larger leakage currents. This can be used to transfer a simple switching action from the input to the output, but with no direct connection between the two. Most opto-isolators can block input to output potentials of 1500 volts or more, and in some cases can withstand peak voltages of several thousand volts.

An opto-isolator of this type can be used to trigger a triac, but there is an easier solution in the form of an opto-triac isolator. This is similar to an ordinary opto-isolator, but it has a triac in place of the transistor. The light from the l.e.d. produces strong leakage currents in the triac, which cause an internal regenerative action that results in the triac turning on. There is no gate current to switch on the triac (and no gate terminal come to that), but the effect of the light from the l.e.d. is effectively the same as a normal gate trigger signal.

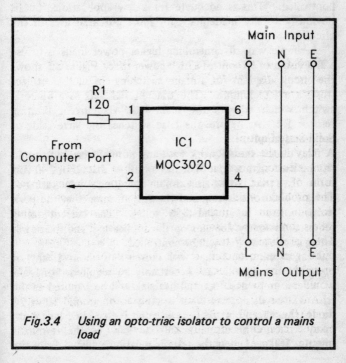

Fig.3.4 *Using an opto-triac isolator to control a mains load*

Figure 3.4 shows the circuit diagram for a computer controlled mains switch using an MOC3020 (or similar) opto-triac isolator. On the input side R1 provides current limiting for the l.e.d. Pin 2 of IC1 is the cathode of the l.e.d., and so it is this terminal that connects to the 0 volt rail of the computer. R1 is fed from a line of the latching digital output port. On the output side the triac is used to switch the "Live" side of the mains supply.

Note that there is no internal connection to pin 3 of the MOC3020. There is an internal connection to pin 5, which connects to the substrate of the triac section of the device. No external connection should be made to this pin.

There is a major limitation to a circuit of this type in that the opto-triac isolator has a very modest current rating of just 100 milliamps. When used on the 240-volt mains supply this means that a maximum power of just 24 watts can be controlled. This is adequate for a few applications, but is obviously totally inadequate for most potential uses of the circuit.

A simple way of controlling higher power loads is to use a triac isolator to control a high power triac. Figure 3.5 shows the circuit diagram for a mains switching circuit that utilizes this slaving technique. The triac in IC1 acts as a bilateral switch which triggers the main triac via current limiting resistor R2. As before, the triac switches the "live" side of the mains supply.

This circuit should work with any normal triac, but should not be used with a triac that has a built-in diac. For 240-volt mains use a triac having a maximum operating voltage rating of at least 400 volts is required (bearing in mind that the peak mains voltage is around 350 volts). The current rating required obviously depends on the application, and the power rating of the load that will be controlled.

Bear in mind here that with currents of about 1 amp or more a heatsink will almost certainly be required. For loads of several amps a substantial heatsink will be required as the triac will be dissipating what is likely to be around 10 or 20 watts. Another point to keep in mind is that the heat-tab on many triacs connects internally to one of the terminals (usually MT2). Unless the triac is reliably insulated from the

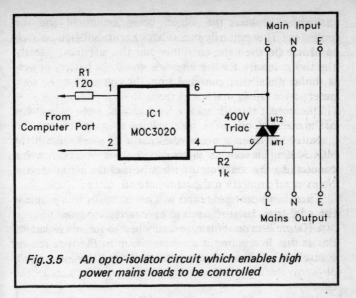

Fig.3.5   An opto-isolator circuit which enables high power mains loads to be controlled

heatsink, the heatsink will also be connected to this terminal (and to the mains supply). **Remember to take all the necessary safety precautions when dealing with any project that connects to the mains supply. Projects that involve the mains supply are not recommended for beginners or those who lack experience.**

Simple Opto-Isolator

While on the subject of opto-isolation it is perhaps worth mentioning that it is sometimes necessary to include opto-isolation on digital inputs or outputs of a computer. There are two common reasons for this, one of which is the need for safety isolation when a computer is used in certain medical electronics applications. This is where someone is connected to electrodes which feed into the computer via an interface unit. This puts them in strong electrical contact with a piece of mains powered equipment (i.e. the computer). If the worst should happen it could be difficult to get the victim disconnected before it was too late. Safety regulations dictate that in such setups an isolation circuit must be included somewhere between the subject being monitored and the computer. This generally means having opto-isolation on each signal line between the computer and the interface. Clearly it is also necessary for the interface unit to be battery powered, rather than being powered from the computer or its own mains power supply unit.

The more common reason for including opto-isolation is that there is a risk of a high voltage existing between the chassis of the computer and the chassis of some other piece of equipment to which it is connected. In my experience this is something that only occurs when neither the computer nor the piece of ancillary equipment have an earthed chassis, but both are mains powered. This will not normally be a problem with a PC, since these all seem to have earthed chassis.

Anyway, if in doubt it is generally best to include isolation, and all that is required is a simple circuit of the type shown in Figure 3.6. This has the usual l.e.d. and current limiting

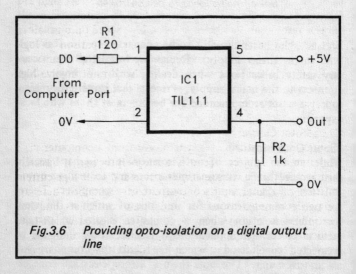

Fig.3.6   Providing opto-isolation on a digital output line

resistor (R1) on the input side, and R2 as the load resistor on the output side. The photo-transistor in IC1 is used as an emitter follower switch. Pin 6 connects to the base terminal of the photo-transistor, but in this circuit no connection is made to the base terminal (there is no internal connection to pin 3 of IC1 incidentally).

Although this circuit is shown as fitting on an output line from the computer, it is quite in order to use it the other way round, with the output of the isolator circuit driving a digital input of the computer. A TIL111 is specified for IC1, but any "bog standard" opto-isolator should work in this circuit. Multiple opto-isolators are available, and usually represent the cheapest and most convenient means of providing isolation on a number of lines. For example, if isolation is required on all eight bits of a digital port, two quad opto-isolators would probably be the best means of providing the isolation.

One final point that has to be made is that opto-isolators are very slow devices by electronic standards. Inexpensive types can generally transfer squarewave signals at frequencies of up to a few kilohertz, but at higher frequencies the output fails to switch properly between logic levels. At high frequencies the output signal simply fails to materialise at all. Better results can be obtained using high speed opto-isolators, but most of these are still very slow in comparison to logic circuits. Simple and inexpensive opto-isolator circuits are only suitable for use in applications that do not involve high frequency signals, which does actually include many computer interfacing applications.

D.C. Motor Control

Control of a small d.c. electric motor from a computer via a digital-to-analogue converter is a simple process. It basically just requires some voltage amplification and some high current buffering. The motor control circuits described here are primarily intended for use as model train controllers, but they can be used to control any d.c. electric motors which have similar power requirements. These circuits are designed to provide a maximum output potential of 12 volts at currents of up to 1 amp.

The larger gauge model trains sometimes require a supply current of up to about 2 amps, and these circuits can handle the extra current provided adequate heatsinking is provided for the output transistor, and the power supply circuit has an

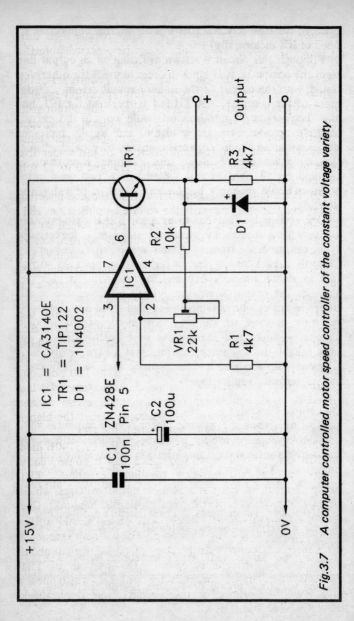

Fig.3.7   A computer controlled motor speed controller of the constant voltage variety

IC1 = CA3140E
TR1 = TIP122
D1 = 1N4002

ZN428E
Pin 5

adequate rating. Note that these circuits require their own mains power supply units, and can not be powered from the PC's supply rails.

Figure 3.7 shows the circuit diagram for a controller of the constant voltage variety. A circuit of this type simply supplies the motor with a variable stabilised voltage. The output voltage range from the ZN426E/428E digital-to-analogue converter is 0 to 2.55 volts. The controller circuit must therefore provide a voltage amplification of just under five times in order to convert this into the required 0 to 12 volt output range.

IC1 is an operational amplifier used in the non-inverting mode, and this stage provides the voltage amplification. R1, R2, and VR1 are the negative feedback circuit which set the voltage gain at the correct level. VR1 must be adjusted to give precisely the required gain of 4.7 times. In practice, the converter is fed with a value of 255 to set the maximum output voltage, and then VR1 is set for the lowest resistance that gives maximum output from the controller.

TR1 is an emitter follower output stage that enables the unit to provide the high output currents required by a d.c. motor. The current drive from IC1 is quite limited, which means that TR1 must provide a very high current gain. A power darlington device is therefore used in the TR1 position, and this gives a current gain of a few thousand times. D1 is a protection diode which suppresses any high reverse voltage spikes that might otherwise be generated across the highly inductive load. R3 is simply a load resistor for TR1.

When building the unit remember that the CA3140E used for IC1 has a PMOS input stage, and that it consequently requires the standard anti-static handling precautions. TR1 has to dissipate several watts at most output voltages, which means that it must be fitted on a substantial heatsink. One having a rating of about 5°C per watt or less should suffice for output currents of up to 1 amp. For a 2 amp version of the circuit a heatsink with a rating of no more than about 2.5°C per watt should be used. The heat-tab of TR1 connects internally to the collector terminal, which means that it will be necessary to insulate TR1 from the heatsink using a TO-220 insulating kit.

In use you will almost certainly find that there is quite a wide range of low values that fail to operate the motor. This is simply because most d.c. electric motors, especially when heavily loaded, require three or four volts before they will start to turn. In some applications it might be necessary to allow for this in the software, with low output values (apart from 0 for "off") being avoided. Although the motor's speed is not continuously variable and it actually has what is likely to be around 200 different speeds, it is unlikely that there will be any obvious change in speed from one control value to the next. This gives what is effectively a continuously variable speed.

Components for Figure 3.7

Resistors (all 0.25 watt 5% carbon film)
R1	4k7
R2	10k
R3	4k7

Potentiometer
VR1	22k miniature preset

Capacitors
C1	100n ceramic
C2	100µ 25V elect

Semiconductors
IC1	CA3140E
TR1	TIP121 or TIP122
D1	1N4002

Miscellaneous
8 pin d.i.l. holder
Heatsink for TR1 (see text)
Case, circuit board, solder, etc.

Pulsed Controller
On the face of it a constant voltage controller will provide perfect results with smooth control of the motor's speed and consistent results. In practice, results using this type of

controller are often not entirely satisfactory. This depends on the particular application, but for use as a model train controller in particular, results can be very disappointing in certain respects. These are the starting and low speed performance.

These problems are not really due to any flaw in the controller, and are largely due to the natural characteristics of small d.c. electric motors. These motors tend to have a reluctance to start, so that quite a high voltage must be applied to a d.c. motor before it will start. Once started, this voltage is sufficient to run the motor at quite high speed. Some motors exhibit this phenomenon more than others, but it seems to be present in all d.c. electric motors to a significant degree. In a model train context it gives the "jump start" effect, where instead of starting and accelerating smoothly, the train suddenly jumps to about one-third speed.

At slow speeds there is a tendency for d.c. motors to stall. Having stalled, it then takes a "jump start" to get them going again. This is a major problem in a computer based system which provides fully automatic control, as the computer will not realise that the train has stalled, and will simply continue to provide the stationary train with low power. If a constant voltage controller is used, probably the best solution is to have an "emergency" key on the keyboard. When pressed, this is detected by a software routine which gives a short burst of full power to the motor. This should spur the motor into action again.

A much better way of handling things is to use a more sophisticated controller which utilizes a system that provides better control of the motor. The most simple route to improved starting and low speed performance is to use a pulsed controller. Rather than having a steady d.c. output signal, a pulse width modulated output signal is used. As we saw with the capacitance measuring interface that was described in Chapter 2, by varying the mark-space ratio of a pulsed d.c. signal the average output voltage can be controlled. A 12-volt d.c. electric motor will work perfectly well from a pulsed d.c. signal, but the output must be at a suitable frequency. In practice quite a wide frequency range gives satisfactory results, but a frequency of around 200Hz to 300Hz generally gives the best results.

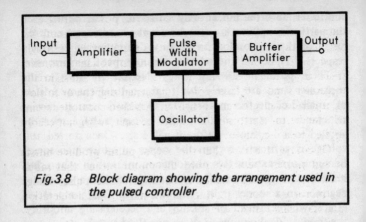

Fig.3.8   Block diagram showing the arrangement used in the pulsed controller

The pulsed controller featured here uses the arrangement shown in the block diagram of Figure 3.8. A clock oscillator operating at a frequency of a few hundred hertz drives a pulse width modulator. The latter provides an output pulse each time it is triggered by the clock oscillator, and the pulse width is controlled by an input voltage. The higher the input voltage, the longer the pulse duration.

In practice things are arranged so that with zero input voltage the output pulses are so short in duration that the output is effectively switched off. With an input of half the supply voltage there is a 1 to 1 mark space ratio at the output, and an average output of half the supply voltage. An input voltage equal to the supply potential gives output pulses that are so long that they almost overlap, giving an almost continuous output voltage equal to the supply potential. The circuit therefore converts a d.c. input level to a pulsed output of equivalent average voltage.

A buffer stage at the output of the circuit enables it to provide the high currents required to drive an electric motor. An amplifier at the input boosts the output from the digital-to-analogue converter to a level that can drive the pulse width modulator properly.

Although a pulsed controller may not offer any obvious advantage over a straightforward constant voltage type, the performance in practice is invariably far superior. The reason

84

for this is that the motor is driven at full power during each output pulse. Even though these pulses are very brief, the fact that they are at full power means that they will strongly resist stalling of the motor. With a constant voltage controller there is often a tendency for the motor to substantially increase its speed if the loading is lightened slightly, or to slow right down if it is increased slightly. A pulsed controller seems to give better performance in this respect, with noticeably better speed regulation.

Of course, the fact that the output pulses produce bursts of full power operation from the motor means that much better starting performance is obtained. The pulses nudge the motor into action, giving smooth starting and acceleration in model train control applications.

Figure 3.9 shows the full circuit diagram for the pulsed train controller. The two standard approaches are to use either operational amplifiers or 555 timers as the basis of the circuit. In terms of cost, performance, and complexity there is not really much to choose between the two methods. As will be apparent from Figure 3.9, in this case I have opted for 555 timers. The circuit is based on a design "borrowed" from my book "Micro Interfacing Circuits Book 2"(BP131).

IC2 operates in the astable mode and acts as the clock oscillator. The only deviation from the standard 555 astable configuration is the inclusion of D1. This provides a very low resistance discharge path for C1, which results in very brief negative going output pulses. It is important that these pulses are very short, since the output pulses from the pulse width modulator can not be shorter than the trigger pulses.

The pulse width modulator utilizes IC3 in what is basically the standard monostable configuration. Normally on each triggering the circuit would operate by having C2 charge to two-thirds of the supply potential via R5. C2 is then rapidly discharged via an internal transistor of IC3. The output at pin 3 goes high during the periods when C2 is being charged. In this case the normally unused pin 5 of IC3 is brought into play, and this modifies the way in which the timing cycle functions. Basically, pin 5 just provides access to the potential divider which sets the two-thirds of the supply voltage threshold level. By pulling this voltage lower each timing cycle is

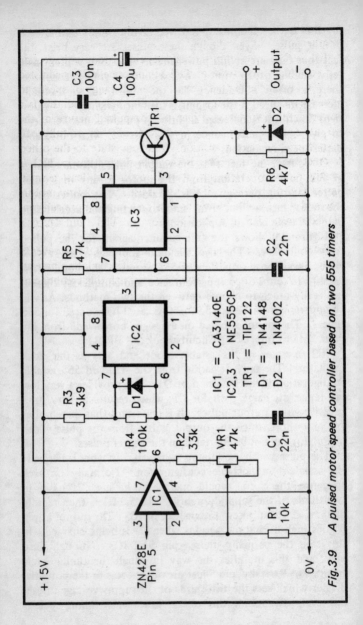

Fig.3.9 A pulsed motor speed controller based on two 555 timers

IC1 = CA3140E
IC2,3 = NE555CP
TR1 = TIP122
D1 = 1N4148
D2 = 1N4002

ZN428E
Pin 5

86

shortened — by taking it higher in voltage each timing cycle is lengthened.

IC1 is the input amplifier, and its closed loop voltage gain can be adjusted by means of VR1. In practice VR1 is adjusted for the lowest value that permits the full range of speeds to be achieved. TR1 is the output buffer stage, and this is a power darlington device. Due to the pulsed nature of the output signal TR1 is always switched fully on or fully off, apart from the brief transitions from one state to the other. A practical benefit of this is that the dissipation in TR1 is greatly reduced. However, it still requires at least a small finned bolt-on heatsink. If the unit is used with 2 amp motors it would be advisable to mount TR1 on a rather more substantial heatsink. R6 is a load resistor for TR1, and D2 is a protection diode.

When building the unit, bear in mind that IC1 has a PMOS input stage, and that the normal anti-static handling precautions are therefore needed when dealing with this component.

Components for Figure 3.9

Resistors (all 0.25 watt 5% carbon film)
R1	10k
R2	33k
R3	3k9
R4	100k
R5	47k
R6	4k7

Potentiometer
VR1	47k miniature preset

Capacitors
C1	22n polyester
C2	22n polyester
C3	100n ceramic
C4	100μ 25V elect

Semiconductors
IC1	CA3140E
IC2	NE555CP

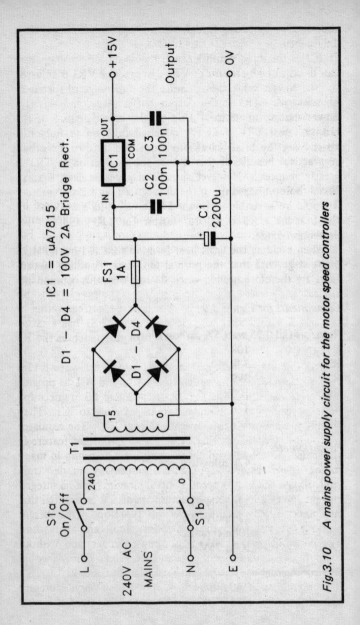

IC1 = uA7815

D1 – D4 = 100V 2A Bridge Rect.

Fig.3.10   A mains power supply circuit for the motor speed controllers

IC3	NE555CP
TR1	TIP121 or TIP122
D1	1N4148
D2	1N4002

Miscellaneous
8 pin d.i.l. i.c. holder (3 off)
Heatsink (see text)
Case, citcuit board, solder, etc.

Mains Power Supply

The PC is unable to provide the +15 volt supply required by the two motor speed controllers, and the controllers must therefore have their own built-in mains power supply unit. For the circuits to operate reliably and safely the supply must be reasonably well smoothed and stabilised. A simple power supply unit such as the one shown in Figure 3.10 is sufficient to drive one amp versions of the circuits. It will also operate as a two amp supply provided the current rating of the mains transformer is at least doubled, FS1 has a rating of 2 amps, and IC1 is a two amp regulator (such as the RS L78S15CV).

The circuit is quite conventional, having full-wave bridge rectification, smoothing provided by C1, and IC1 to provide electronic smoothing and regulation. C2 and C3 are decoupling capacitors which should be mounted close to IC1. They should then ensure stable operation from IC1. The regulator has built-in current limiting, which is an important feature in this case. Overloads and short circuits are common in many motor speed control applications, especially model train control. As the motor speed control circuits have no integral current limiting or other protection circuits, it is essential that the power supply circuit fulfils this function. This current limiting protects both the controller circuit and the motor. The controller is probably in the most danger, and without the current limiting it is likely that even brief overloads would destroy the output transistor in the controller circuit.

Construction of the power supply circuit should present few difficulties, but as the mains supply is involved it is vital to observe the usual safety precautions. The circuit should be housed in a case of all-metal construction and it should be reliably earthed to the mains earth lead. The lid or cover must be a screw fixing type, and not one that simply unclips or slides out. Make sure that you never come into contact with any of the mains wiring.

IC1 must be fitted on a medium sized heatsink. In practice it is probably easier to simply mount it on the metal case which should provide more than adequate heatsinking. There is no need to use an insulating set on IC1 since its heat-tab connects internally to the "common" terminal. This connects to the 0 volt supply rail (and hence to the metal casing) anyway.

Components for Figure 3.10

Hardware
T1	Mains primary, 15 volt 1.5 amp secondary
S1	Rotary on/off mains switch

Semiconductors
IC1	7815 (15 volt 1 amp positive regulator)
D1 – D4	100 volt 2 amp bridge rectifier

Capacitors
C1	2200μ 40V elect
C2	100n ceramic
C3	100n ceramic

Fuse
FS1	20mm 1 amp quick-blow

Miscellaneous
Output sockets, case, circuit board, heatsink for IC1, solder, etc.

Direction Control

The direction of a d.c. electric motor is controlled by the polarity of the applied voltage. In a model train controller application, or any other application that requires direction control via the computer, some switching is needed at the output of the controller. Basically all that is needed is a relay driver and a relay having twin changeover contacts. The latter are wired in the manner shown in Figure 3.11. The

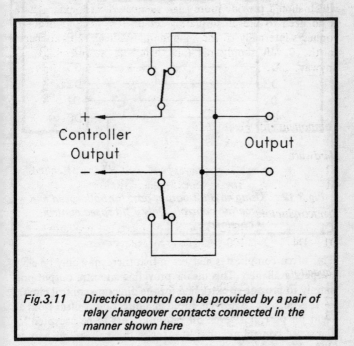

Fig.3.11   Direction control can be provided by a pair of relay changeover contacts connected in the manner shown here

contacts must be of the break before make variety, and not the make before break type (which would short circuit the output of the controller on each changeover). All the relays I have ever used have been equipped with break before make contacts, but it is worthwhile checking this point just in case.

When using a motor speed controller plus the direction control circuit it is obviously necessary to have nine output lines (eight for speed control and one for direction control).

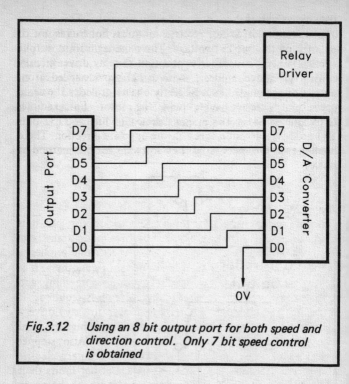

Fig.3.12   Using an 8 bit output port for both speed and
direction control. Only 7 bit speed control
is obtained

This often complicates matters in that there may only be eight
outputs available. This means providing an extra output port
simply to provide an extra line for the direction control circuit.

It is possible to provide speed and direction control from an
eight bit port, but seven bit resolution has to be accepted for
the speed control circuit. In practice this will still give something like a hundred different speeds, which provides quite
fine speed control. This permits smooth acceleration and
deceleration of a model train with no obvious jumping from
one speed to the next.

The basic method of using an eight bit port for both types
of control is shown in Figure 3.12. The basic scheme of
things is to have the lower seven bits of the port drive the
upper seven inputs of the digital-to-analogue converter. There
is no output available to drive the least significant input of the

converter which is therefore connected to earth. This reduces the maximum output voltage to 2.54 volts, but this is not of any real importance in practice. The most significant output is free for use with the direction control relay driver circuit.

With this system values from 0 to 127 provide speeds from zero to maximum. Adding 128 to a value provides the same speed, but reverses the direction of the motor. For example, 32 provides a low speed in one direction, while 160 (32 plus 128) provides the same speed in the opposite direction. There should be no difficulty in writing software for this method of control.

Stepper Motor Driver

A stepper motor is a form of d.c. electric motor, but it is totally different to the motors used to drive model trains, etc. The most important difference is that, as its name implies, a stepper motor is stepped from one position to another. It is used where it is necessary to precisely position something, and not normally used where continuous rotation is required. It would be possible to use a stepper motor to (say) drive a model train, but it would definitely be doing things the hard way, and would provide no obvious advantage. Also, stepper motors tend to be far less powerful than ordinary electric motors less than half their size. This somewhat limits their practical use, and is something that needs to be borne in mind when contemplating the use of a stepper motor.

There are actually several types of stepper motor, but the type we are concerned with here is the four phase type. These motors have four electro-magnets, and they are all powered continuously in use. By altering the polarities of the electro-magnets, the motor can be stepped from one position to the next. Figure 3.13 shows the basic way in which a stepper motor operates.

Remembering that unlike poles attract and like poles repel, it can be seen that by switching the polarities of the four electro-magnets in the manner shown, the permanent magnet (the one at the centre, which is free to rotate) can be dragged from one position to the next. By reversing the sequence the magnet can be stepped in the opposite direction.

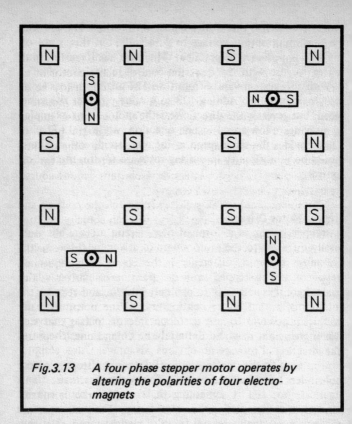

*Fig.3.13   A four phase stepper motor operates by
            altering the polarities of four electro-
            magnets*

This setup is quite complex to control in that there are four
electromagnets, and it must be possible to reverse the signal to
each one so that its polarity can be reversed. In practice things
are simplified by having the four magnetic poles provided by
two electro-magnets in a sort of cross formation. This is an
acceptable way of doing things since, as can be seen from
Figure 3.13, each pole is of the opposite polarity to the one
physically opposite to it. A further simplification is to have
two anti-phase windings on each electro-magnet. This enables
the polarity of each electro-magnet to be altered simply by
switching from one coil to the other. A real stepper motor
therefore has four coils, but only two of the four coils are

actually switched on at any one time, and there are still four electro-magnetic poles.

A stepper motor based on this method has a resolution of 90 degrees. While this does not render such a motor of no practical value, control in smaller steps would clearly be an advantage, and make life easier when using stepper motors in many practical situations. "Real life" four phase stepper motors use more electro-magnets and magnetic poles to obtain higher resolution, but retain exactly the same method of control. A resolution of 7.5 or 15 degrees is typical for one of these motors. Higher effective resolutions can, of course, be obtained using step down gearing.

The stepper motor controller must switch the coils on and off in the appropriate manner, and this can actually be done without resorting to a special driver circuit. The coils could be driven via relay driver type circuits, with software in the computer switching the coils in the appropriate sequences. However, it is generally easier to use a special driver as this greatly simplifies the software side of things, and reduces the number of output lines needed to control the motor. It really only requires two lines: one to provide the pulses that step the motor from one position to the next, and one to control the direction of rotation.

Figure 3.14 shows the circuit diagram for a stepper motor controller based on the SAA1027 integrated circuit. This device is not exactly the last word in stepper motor control circuits, but it does have its advantages. The main ones are that it is well established, readily available, and relatively inexpensive.

It also provides a perfectly adequate level of performance. It does not incorporate any form of power economy circuit. In other words, the power is always applied to two windings of the motor, even during periods of inactivity. This is not normally necessary, and it is unlikely that the motor position will tend to drift if none of the coils are not energised. On the other hand, it is unlikely that there will be any great advantage in powering-down the motor during periods of inactivity unless the circuit is battery powered. In the vast majority of cases the motor will be powered from a mains power supply circuit though.

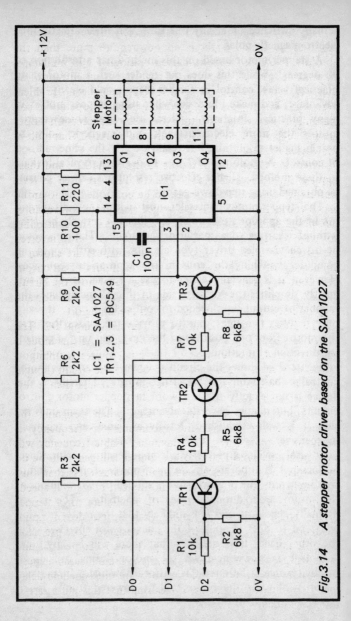

Fig.3.14   A stepper motor driver based on the SAA1027

The four outputs of IC1 can directly drive the stepper motor coils provided these do not require more than the absolute maximum output current rating of 500 milliamps. In practice it would be better to have an output current of no more than 350 milliamps, and there should be no problem here as 12-volt stepper motors mainly seem to operate at coil currents of much less than this. No discrete protection diodes are included at the outputs because the SAA1027 has built-in protection diodes.

There are three control inputs to the SAA1027, and these require 12-volt logic signals. TR1 to TR3 are used as level shifters which enable the circuit to be controlled using ordinary 5-volt logic levels. These stages also provide inversions, but this is of no great practical consequence. The controlling software simply has to be tailored to suit this inverted method of control. In Figure 3.14 the inputs are shown as connecting to the three least significant inputs of an output port, but this is only done as an example of how the circuit can be controlled. Any three latching outputs will do, and they do not even have to be lines from the same port.

The pulses to step the motor are applied to input D2. The motor is stepped on low to high transitions. As this input is edge triggered, the duration of the input pulses is unimportant. Very short pulses could be missed by the circuit though, and it is probably best to use pulses of no less than a few microseconds in duration.

A crucial point to keep in mind when designing the control software is that the maximum step frequency is likely to be quite low. The maximum usable frequency will vary from one motor to another, but it will generally be no more than 20 to 30 hertz, and might be much less than this. Although ordinary d.c. electric motors can operate at speeds of up to a few thousand r.p.m., the maximum for a stepper motor could well be no more than a few dozen r.p.m. Remember that these motors are designed for precision control, not for high speed or high power. Some trial and error will be needed to determine the maximum usable speed for a given application, and the software must include delay loops or some other means of ensuring that this pulse rate is never exceeded.

D1 is the direction control input, and with the motor connected to IC1 correctly it will rotate in a clockwise direction with D1 high, and in an anti-clockwise direction when it is low.

Input D0 is the reset input, and taking this high resets the four outputs of IC1 to their initial state. Note that this is not the same as taking the motor back to its initial position – it simply resets the outputs to one of their four sets of output states. In a practical application the software normally needs to keep count of the pulses sent to the motor. This can be done using simple software routine to provide a counter action, and a byte or two of RAM to store the answer. The motor's position can then be determined from the value in the counter. If two way operation is used, then pulses to move the motor in one direction must increment the counter, while pulses to move it in the other direction must decrement the counter.

There is a flaw in this system in that it is possible for something to temporarily block the motor so that its true position is out of step with the notional position read from the counter. There is no easy way around this, and a feedback mechanism to check movement of the motor is likely to be far too complex and costly to implement. The only practical course of action is to make sure, as far as possible, that nothing blocks the motor. Also, make sure that there is an easy way of getting things back into synchronisation if they should go wrong.

It is obviously essential for the stepper motor to be connected correctly if everything is to function correctly. I used a Maplin stepper motor which has coloured coded flying leads. These are connected in the manner shown in Table 2. Note that there are only two leads which connect to the +12 volt supply, and not four. This is quite common, and is due to the way that the pairs of windings are wound on each pole piece. Of course, other four phase stepper motors will almost certainly use a different method of coding the leads, but the retailer should provide connection information with any stepper motor.

Table 2

Colour	Connection Point
Green	+12V
Green	+12V
Blue	IC1 Q1
Yellow	IC1 Q2
Red	IC1 Q3
White	IC1 Q4

Components for Figure 3.14

Resistors (all 0.25 watt 5% carbon film unless noted)

R1	10k
R2	6k8
R3	2k2
R4	10k
R5	6k8
R6	2k2
R7	10k
R8	6k8
R9	2k2
R10	100R
R11	220R 1 watt

Capacitor

C1	100n ceramic

Semiconductors

TR1	BC549
TR2	BC549
TR3	BC549
IC1	SAA1027

Miscellaneous
14 pin d.i.l. i.c. holder
Four phase stepper motor (Maplin FT73Q or similar)
Circuit board, case, solder, etc.

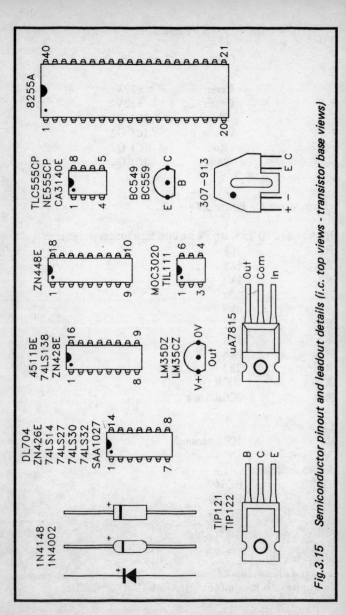

Fig.3.15 Semiconductor pinout and leadout details (i.c. top views - transistor base views)

100

If you would like a complete catalogue of our entire range of Radio, Electronics and Computer Books then please send a Stamped Addressed Envelope to:

BERNARD BABANI (publishing) LTD
THE GRAMPIANS
SHEPHERDS BUSH ROAD
LONDON W6 7NF
ENGLAND